THE HANDICAPPED CHILDREN

OF

ALAMANCE COUNTY
NORTH CAROLINA

A Medical and Sociological Study

WILLIAM P. RICHARDSON, M.D., M.P.H., *Professor of Preventive Medicine and Assistant Dean, School of Medicine University of North Carolina*

A. C. HIGGINS, PH.D., *Lecturer, Department of Sociology and Anthropology, and Director, Cardiac Rehabilitation Project, Syracuse University, Syracuse, New York*

in collaboration with

RICHARD G. AMES, M.A., *Instructor in Sociology University of North Carolina*

PUBLISHED BY THE NEMOURS FOUNDATION, WILMINGTON, DELAWARE

THE HANDICAPPED CHILDREN OF
ALAMANCE COUNTY, NORTH CAROLINA:
A MEDICAL AND SOCIOLOGICAL STUDY

Printed and Bound by
Christian Printing Company, Durham, N. C., U.S.A.

SPONSORS

STUDY STAFF

STUDY ADVISORY COMMITTEE

OUTLINE OF THIS BOOK

This book is made up of several discrete articles, each focusing on some aspect of the socio-medical problems of the handicapped child. Each article developed out of the three-year study of Alamance County, North Carolina, and deals with relatively limited aspects of the whole. Together they help in understanding many of the interrelated problems of the handicapped child, his family and his community.

The first two chapters deal with "overviews" of the whole study: the first concerns what might be called the "background" of the study; the second, the morbidity rates, the data, presented as a whole. Part Two is concerned with the "agency phase," Part Three with the household survey, and Part Four with the special clinics and some insights they provide concerning broad aspects of the problem. Part Five presents a summary and some recommendations for future action.

In view of the manner in which these reports were written, it was felt necessary to provide the reader with points of transition, brief statements indicating the relationship between the articles. These statements are presented separated by blank pages in the text for easy recognition.

ACKNOWLEDGMENTS

A project like this involves many people and agencies. It is not possible to acknowledge each individual by name, but we are grateful for the wholehearted cooperation which was given freely by every person and organization whose help was requested.

The study was financed by a grant from the Nemours Foundation of Wilmington, Delaware, and Doctor A. R. Shands, Jr., Medical Director of the Foundation gave invaluable advice and encouragement. Additional financial assistance was provided by United Cerebral Palsy of North Carolina and the School of Medicine of the University of North Carolina.

Staff members of the Institute for Research in Social Science and the School of Medicine were most generous in their assistance. Special thanks go to the physicians and professional associates who took part in the clinical examinations. The greater number of these were from the staff of the University of North Carolina School of Medicine. Also assisting were psychologists from the State Department of Public Welfare, local physicians, physicians from the State Board of Health and from the Department of Pediatrics of the Duke University School of Medicine.

Mr. Gerard S. Anderson, Mrs. Prue E. Edwards, Mr. J. Minetree Pyne and Dr. Paul F. Maness gave indispensable assistance in many phases of the study, devoting time and effort far beyond the call of duty. Others whose helpful cooperation is greatly appreciated are Mr. Calvin C. Linneman, Mrs. Doris W. Nichols, Dr. W. L. Norville, Dr. L. Everett Spikes, Mr. A. Howard White, Mrs. Rebecca Whiteneck, and the members of the staff of the Alamance County Department of Public Welfare who did the social interviewing for all the children who were examined in the clinics. We are grateful to the many volunteers from Alamance County who participated in the household survey phase, and especially to Mrs. Ella B. Kerr and Mrs. Edith Saunders who recruited them and organized their efforts.

In addition to these individuals we are grateful for the cooperation of the following organizations in Alamance County: Alamance County Welfare Department, Alamance County Mental Health Authority, Alamance County Health Department, Community Council of Burlington, the Burlington City Schools and Alamance County Schools, Alamance County Hospital, Alamance Memorial Hospital, Alamance County Medical Society, Alamance County Dental Society, and various voluntary health organizations.

Cooperation of various state agencies is gratefully acknowledged: Department of Mental Health, Department of Correction and Training, State Board of Health, State Department of Public Welfare, Department of Public Instruction, State Commission for the Blind, and Division of Vocational Rehabilitation. We also appreciate the cooperation of the North Carolina Memorial Hospital, Chapel Hill, and Duke Hospital, Durham.

In Halifax County we are very grateful for the cooperation of Dr. Robert Young and his staff at the Health Center, as well as the many volunteers who participated in the household survey there.

Finally, we wish to thank the American Journal of Public Health for permission to use the material in articles published in the July, August, and November, 1964 issues of that Journal.

TABLE OF CONTENTS

LIST OF TABLES

PART I

THE PICTURE IN PERSPECTIVE

CHAPTER I

BACKGROUND, OBJECTIVES AND DEFINITIONS

This is a book about handicapped children. Its major focus is the presentation of statistics concerning morbidity in persons under twenty-one years of age. Throughout, data are presented which are designed to assist North Carolinians and others in meeting the needs of a segment of the population for which communities generally seek to provide assistance.

The statistics provided are useful to the extent that they serve to describe the social situation in which handicapped children exist. In other words, the statistics are designed to provide insight into the ways youngsters are treated: inferentially, they tell us something about the behaviors of people responsible for the care of children.

This is not, then, simply a statistical report of several surveys of morbidity. Such statistical reports, albeit limited, are available from a variety of sources.[1] On the contrary, this is a medical and sociological report dealing with an important aspect of medical care in North Carolina. These data help to provide insight and it is only in this sense that they acquire meaning and become useful.

Putting data to use does not necessarily mean new buildings, more physicians, or a new health facility for handling children with special needs. These may well come eventually, but initially data should be the basis for careful planning, not of hasty action. All too often new data, like new money, lead to ill-advised waste.

The more or less structured interpretation in this analysis is one which relies on both medical and sociological perspectives. This book represents the collaboration of efforts of physicians and sociologists. It is acknowledged that both medical and social facts are to be viewed as creating problems, difficulties and imbalances in the recognition, treatment and rehabilitation of children who are defined as handicapped. One purpose, therefore, is to point to some of the difficulties and contradictions in the special field of health related to handicapped children, and to determine and describe the social struc-

---

1. Commission on Chronic Illness, *Chronic Illness in a Large City.* Cambridge, Massachusetts: Harvard University Press, 1957, Vol. 4. All of the materials published in the U. S. National Health Survey are also relevant; see particularly, Health Statistics from the U. S. National Health Survey Reports, Series C, No. 1. Children and Youth: Selected Health Characteristics. Public Health Service, Washington, D. C. 1959.

tures in the community relevant to the understanding of the physically, emotionally and mentally handicapped child.

The data to be examined are derived from an intensive study of Alamance County, North Carolina. The geographical limitation permitted the examination of operating health facilities in a more or less "typical" community and, furthermore, it permitted the examination of several interesting methodological considerations.

Many questions are raised by this research effort and very few answers provided. Those who plan to provide answers will need all the information they can get. It is our hope that this information will be of service to them.

Background of the Study

The North Carolina Survey of Handicapped Children began in 1959 with the recognition that from the standpoint of information *readily available* in 1959, data necessary for basic planning was incomplete, fragmentary and often misleading. This recognition was fostered by the attempt to make long range plans in North Carolina for caring for handicapped children. Beginning in 1954, under the auspices of the Nemours Foundation of Wilmington, Delaware, a series of conferences on children with special needs had been held in the state. To these meetings had come experts in dealing with handicapped children. Their experiences and their different points of view had served to emphasize the inadequacy of existing information on handicapping conditions and to create a desire for more precise information.

It was Dr. A. R. Shands, Jr., Medical Director of the Nemours Foundation, who approached the Coordinating Committee on Children with Special Needs regarding a foundation-supported project to gather the needed basic information. Two considerations influenced Dr. Shands in his selection of North Carolina for the proposed study. The first was the aggregation of resources and experiences available in the University of North Carolina through the Schools of Medicine and Public Health and the Institute for Research in Social Science. The second, a consideration of particular interest to North Carolinians, was the tremendous interest and cooperation which were being manifested in North Carolina in studying and attempting to meet the health and social needs of its people.

It was originally thought possible to study three "representative" North Carolina counties to give a cross section of the mountains, Piedmont and coastal plain. However, it was found to be unfeasible to study more than one county in any detail—the problems were so complex that this optimistic objective had to be limited. The advisory committee decided that only one community should be studied and that it should be close to Chapel Hill, large enough to give a good cross section of rural, industrial and urban population, have a wide range of active community organization, and have given indications of the kind of interest and cooperation needed. In the light of these considerations Alamance County was chosen as the area in which the study would be undertaken.

The initial objectives of the study were:

1) To determine the prevalence of various handicapping conditions among children, including variations in prevalence, if such exist, among different segments of the population.
2) To evaluate the extent of disability caused by these conditions, and the factors other than the conditions themselves which help determine the degree of disability.
3) To evaluate the effectiveness of various methods of determining the prevalence of handicapping conditions in a community and, particularly, to evaluate the adequacy and inadequacies of information available from existing files and registers at the local and state levels.
4) To evaluate factors other than availability of services which influence whether or not handicapped children receive the care they need.
5) To determine the services and facilities needed to provide optimum care and rehabilitation for these children, to measure the adequacy of available services and facilities and to make recommendations as to unmet needs.

Not all of these objectives have been fully met. In the three years since the field work began, emphasis, interests and problems have shifted and changed. Information relevant to each of the objectives mentioned above is available in this report but the major focus has been on objectives 1, 3, and 4.

The design of the survey included three major steps. First, a thorough study was made of existing medical and paramedical records. This included the data available in published and unpublished statistical reports issued by state or local agencies and the materials contained in the record files of physicians in private practice. No agency dealing with the children of Alamance County was eliminated or bypassed. The completion of this examination of records revealed the prevalence of handicapping conditions *according to the service facilities of the county.*

Second, the study designed and completed a survey of a sample of households of the county. This survey focused on the extent to which handicapping conditions were perceived by a random sample of parents. This gave a second definition of the handicapped children of the county, the morbidity rates *according to the parents of the county*.

Third, the staff conducted a diagnostic clinic in which subsamples of children reported to be handicapped by service facilities and by parents were thoroughly examined. In order to estimate the degree of underreporting, children who were reportedly normal were also invited. The definition of handicapped children used in this clinic stage was morbidity *according to the examining physicians*.

There were, then, three phases to the overall study. The "agency phase" continued from October, 1961, through November, 1962, during which registers from state, local and private agencies were examined. A list containing names, medical conditions, background factors, and other relevant data, was prepared containing 5,953 entries concerning 4,083 children. (Individual children may have been known to more than one agency.) The second phase, the "household survey," gathered information on 1,684 children, approximately a five per cent sample of the population under 21 years of age. With the help of volunteer workers in the county, this household survey phase was completed in March, 1962.* The third phase, the "diagnostic clinic," examined 456 children in 26 working days in the period between April and August, 1962.*

Definitions

What has been said concerning research design makes it clear that differing definitions of "handicapped children" were used in the different phases of the study. It is, therefore, necessary at this point to try to clarify this question of definition.

Unfortunately, it is not so simple as setting down a succinct statement of criteria and defining all who meet these as "handicapped" and all who do not as "normal" or "not handicapped." The concept of the handicapped child which forms the basis of the study is that set forth in the definition offered by the American Public Health Association.[2]

> A child is considered to be handicapped if he cannot within limits play, learn, work or do the things other children of his age can do; if he is hindered in achieving his full physical, mental

---

* The forms used are presented in the Appendix.
2. Committee on Child Health, American Public Health Association. Services for Handicapped Children. New York, 1961, p. 12.

and social potentialities. The initial disability may be very mild and hardly noticeable, but potentially handicapping, or it may seriously involve several areas of function with the probability of lifelong impairment. The problem may appear to be primarily physical, or perhaps emotional or social. Regardless of the nature of the chief manifestations, physical, emotional and social components are all factors at one time or another and in varying degrees, in most handicapping conditions of childhood.

This statement, however, presents notable difficulties as a working definition. For example, how is determination to be made that a "hardly noticeable" disability is "potentially handicapping"? How is the handicap of such social factors as poverty and race to be measured?

It was necessary, therefore, to set up operational definitions. For this purpose we chose to define a handicapped child in each phase of the study as a child recognized or defined as handicapped by the individual or agencies who provided the information sought in that phase. These, of course, were distinct for each phase. In the review of agency records the definitions were those of the workers who prepared and maintained the files of health agencies serving the county. In the household survey they were those of the parents who were interviewed. In the clinical examinations the examining physicians were responsible for the categorization, "normal" or "handicapped" and for the specific diagnoses.

An understanding of some of the factors which go into the definition of a child as handicapped by the several information sources is necessary for proper evaluation of the information derived from each. The term "handicapped child" is a label by which the person who uses it places the child in a category in accord with his concept of the term. Naming or defining is not a *description* of what is reality but an *interpretation* of reality in the perspective of the namer. Definitions or labels may, when viewed in this way, tell us as much about the namers as about the reality of the situation.

Suppose, for example, that the records of health agencies of a community show that the distribution of mental health problems by race and sex is unequal, Negro females having the fewest emotional problems. What does this mean? It is possible the recorded distribution indicates as much about the values of those who make the designation as about the children in question. On the basis of similar patterns of behavior the white female may be classified as "sick" and the Negro female as "not sick" because of differential expectations for the white and Negro child. Such a differential is not simply prejudice; it results from a variety of social factors. Only by understanding the community can insight be gained into the way these differential expectations are distributed.

The records of physicians and health agencies include, of course, only those children who have been brought to them as individuals, for whom some care has been sought. An important question, then, becomes, why are children brought or not brought to the attention of physicians or appropriate community agencies? What factors promote or inhibit the provision of medical care? What are parental concepts of health and illness? How are physicians viewed by parents *vis-a-vis* the child? What are the images of the health agencies of the community? How do these concepts and images influence the seeking of needed attention? The records of health agencies and information gathered from parents themselves may help provide answers to these questions.

One feature of this study, then, is an attempt to compare the defining procedures employed by the three information sources used, to interpret the differences in rates of handicapping conditions derived from these sources in terms of the factors which enter into the different definitions, and to determine the implications of differences in definition for community programs designed to meet the needs of handicapped children.

Alamance County

The area selected for study is a fairly prosperous county in the west central Piedmont of North Carolina. Its population was 85,674 according to the 1960 Census, and at the time of the survey was estimated to be 89,100.[3] Approximately 17 per cent of its population is non-white. There were 36,500 persons, 41 per cent, under 21 years of age.

The county ranks fifth in the state in per capita income, $1,800. Sixty per cent of Negro families and 15 per cent of the white families of the county have incomes of less than $3,000. The majority of white males (60%) are occupied in blue collar jobs, with 6 per cent engaged in farming. Almost 20 per cent of Negro males are occupied in farming.

Comparing Alamance County to the other 99 counties of the state in terms of various indexes of social disorganization, it is found

---

3. Population projections to June, 1962, were prepared by Mr. Josef Perry, Division of Community Planning, Department of Conservation and Development, Raleigh, North Carolina.

that it ranks 31st in the distribution of juvenile delinquency rates, 75th in Negro illegitimacy. It has a relatively low school drop-out rate and ranks 64th in the state. Ninety-three per cent of its citizens admitted to State Hospitals for emotional disturbances have been white. Only 5 per cent of its State Hospital admissions have been children under 19 years of age. It ranked 12th in the state in 1961-62 in the number of admissions to State Hospitals and 7th in the state in readmission rates.[4] There is a concentration of people and centralization of services in the City of Burlington. Burlington, with its neighbors of Graham, Haw River and Elon College, includes about 63 per cent of the population of the county. Burlington is the home of Burlington Industries which has 11 of its mills located in or near the city. The city has one of the heaviest concentrations of textile mills in the Piedmont, and fully 40 per cent of the labor force works in yarn, fabric or knitting mills. Another large employer is Western Electric, located in Burlington since 1946, and employing over 4,000 workers.

There are two school systems in the county: Burlington City Schools and Alamance County Schools. The former had an average daily enrollment of almost 9,000 and the latter, almost 11,700 for 1961-62. Approximately 60 per cent of the population under 21 years of age is enrolled in one or the other of these two systems.

Medical services available in the county are centralized in Burlington which is the home of the two hospitals in the county. It is the site of the Health and Welfare Departments and the Mental Health Clinic, and 54 of the 68 registered physicians in the county are located in the city.

The Conditions Studied

The categories of disability studied in this report on Alamance County included these thirteen conditions:

Orthopedic conditions	Mental retardation
Epilepsy	Respiratory disorders
Vision defects	Heart conditions
Hearing defects	Orthodontic conditions
Cleft lip or palate	Cerebral palsy
Emotional disturbance	Skin conditions
Speech disorders	

---

4. The Planning Staff of the North Carolina Mental Health Council, Supplement Number One of the Comprehensive Mental Health Planning Guide, *Base Line Data for Planning: County Profiles.* Raleigh, North Carolina, January, 1964.

Two additional categories of health had to be included. The first of these is a residual "other" category which included all handicapping conditions not otherwise specified. The other is a category of "normal" children concerning whom no presumptive diagnosis of handicapping condition was made.

Health statistics are generally reported in terms of conditions rather than numbers of children affected but it would be possible to report these materials in either way. For the sake of consistency the statistics will be presented in terms of conditions rather than children since medical service facilities are structured toward the servicing of conditions rather than children. Such services generally make little attempt to provide care for the "whole child."

The following brief descriptions of each of the conditions are provided to give the reader some idea of the kinds of disorders included under each term in the list presented. They are not necessarily adequate as clinical descriptions of the conditions.[5]

> **Orthopedic and neuromuscular conditions.** Any abnormality of structure or function of the bones, joints or muscles. Some specific conditions included were: missing arms, legs, fingers, toes; scoliosis; arthritis; tibial torsion, etc. (Not included in this category were cerebral palsied children, a condition described below.)
>
> **Epilepsy.** A condition characterized by recurrent convulsions or related episodes; or by a number of convulsions that are believed to be more than the common febrile reactions of early childhood or the transient symptoms of acute infection or injury. (This included a variety of convulsive disorders in addition to so-called idiopathic epilepsy.)
>
> **Vision defects.** Any significant abnormality of structure, position or function of the eyelid or any part of the eyeball; visual acuity of less than 20/40 when corrected.
>
> **Hearing defects.** Any conditions involving a functional hearing loss in the 500-2000 cycle range demonstrable by audiometric examination or where there is gross hearing impairment.
>
> **Cleft lip or palate.** Any appreciable cleft of the palate or lip; a significant sequela of a treated cleft.
>
> **Emotional disturbance.** Any gross deviation in personal behavior or social relationships.

---

5. The Present study is deeply indebted to Dr. Samuel M. Wishik of the School of Public Health, The University of Pittsburgh, for his encouragement, insight and acumen. The definitions which are provided clearly reflect Dr. Wishik's pioneering work in Georgia. See: Samuel M. Wishik, "Handicapped Children in Georgia: A Study of Prevalence, Disability, Needs and Resources," *American Journal of Public Health,* 46 (February, 1956), pp. 195-203.

Speech disorders. Any definite abnormality in development, fluency or clarity of speech; younger children with gross speech disturbance from organic cause, such as cleft palate.

Mental retardation. Any gross delay in development which is believed to be due, at least in part, to mental factors. For children diagnosed by psychometric tests, an IQ below 70.

Chronic respiratory disorders. Recurrent impairment of breathing, or cough, with or without obvious external change in the thoracic cage. Specific conditions include asthma with or without hay fever, bronchitis, cystic fibrosis and tuberculosis.

Heart conditions. Congenital or acquired structural or functional abnormality of the heart or blood vessels.

Orthodontic conditions. Significant malocclusion of the permanent teeth, or gross abnormality of the structure or appearance of the jaw or teeth.

Cerebral palsy. Any motor disturbance of the body apparently due to a previous and reasonably static type of damage of the central nervous system above the level of the spinal cord.

Skin conditions. Any chronic or recurring skin condition which presents an unsightly appearance if on usually exposed areas of the body, including the face; or, if on any area of the body, interferes with the usual activity and body hygiene by reason of discomfort or threat of infection and which can be controlled, if at all, only by continual use of medical treatment. Specific conditions include atopic eczema (chronic), seborrheic eczema (chronic), contact dermatitis (excluding poison ivy dermatitis and psoriasis).

Other. Any conditions not included in the above listing which either a health agency, a concerned parent or an examining physician judged to present chronic difficulties to the child. Specific conditions include: uncertain diagnoses (where the physician refused to make judgment as to the condition); glandular disturbance; diseases of the blood; cancer.

Normal. The absence of judgments of health agencies, physicians or parents as to abnormality of the child.

The following very important specification is in order: these very brief descriptions were not necessarily employed by health agents, physicians or by parents. Medical agencies have their own definitions of handicapped children which would have to be specified for each health agency and, probably, for each worker within the agency. Physicians use variable criteria for the placement of children in this, that, or the other category. Parents' judgments with respect to the health of their children are probably subject to a great many factors. It is to be noted that the study was interested in discerning all those conditions which may be viewed as disabling to the child.

CHAPTER II

THE STUDY: PROCEDURES AND BASIC DATA*

Three methods of data gathering are generally used for estimating morbidity in the United States: the examination of medical records,[1] the use of health questionnaires,[2] and clinical examinations.[3] It is known that these techniques generate different morbidity estimates[4] in that they measure different phenomena: medical records report services by health agents, surveys obtain individual or familial awareness of medical conditions, and clinical examinations provide estimates of professional recognition of disabilities. These are three somewhat distinct and yet overlapping dimensions of the complex area of illness, disability and health services.

Different techniques will undoubtedly produce different sets of morbidity rates. Such differences tend to be confusing to professional and lay people alike, and create problems when health plans and programs must be based on such statistics. The present study is not designed to provide "absolute" values or parameters for handicapping conditions; it is, in part, designed to present estimates of morbidity in a single geographic area and to specify the "order of magnitude" by which different techniques of measurement introduce bias into estimated morbidity rates.

In Alamance County these three techniques of estimating morbidity were employed: a review of the registers containing information developed by health agencies; a household survey; and then, a diagnostic clinical examination of subsamples of both normal and presumptively handicapped children. The findings of these efforts should not only be descriptive of Alamance County but generalizable to several other counties of the state. At the minimum there is no

---

* Original article including much of this material appeared in the November, 1964, issue of the *American Journal of Public Health.* Copyright 1964, American Public Health Association, Inc.

1. Bureau of the Census, National Office of Vital Statistics, *Vital Statistics of the United States.* Washington, D. C.: Government Printing Office, published annually.

2. All of the materials of the U. S. National Health Survey are relevant. See: U. S. National Health Survey. Origin and Program of the U. S. National Health Survey. Health Statistics. Series A-1. Public Health Service Publication No. 584-A1. Public Health Service, Washington, D. C.: May, 1958.

3. Commission on Chronic Illness. *Chronic Illness in a Large City.* Cambridge, Massachusetts: Harvard University Press, 1957.

4. Ray E. Trussell, Jack Ellisson, Jr., and Morton L. Levin, "Comparisons of Various Methods of Estimating the Prevalence of Chronic Disease in a Community—The Hunterdon County Study," *American Journal of Public Health* 46 (February, 1956), pp. 173-182.

13

reason to think that Alamance County is atypical of the Piedmont area of North Carolina. Probably more important than the extrapolations made from these data is an understanding of the factors influencing the statistics. The social facts affecting medical practices in Alamance County afford valid insights into the complex problems related to handicapped children and their care in many areas of the United States.

We began this research looking for useful statistics concerning handicapped children and found, in the search, useful information regarding the ways in which physicians and their associates, parents, and health agencies function in this community. The question became in the course of research not what statistics are valid; but rather, how do they come into being and what do they reveal about the health of Alamance County from the sociological perspective.

The Agency Review

The most important feature of the review of the medical records on the children of Alamance County is that it attempted to examine every record for all children resident in the county. This means that it is possible to report prevalence estimates based on the population projections for June, 1962. It is assumed here that such use of the total population as a base is possible despite the fact that there were some exceptions to complete coverage of the records.

Complete coverage was impossible for a variety of reasons. Physicians in private practice, for example, could not be expected to recall from memory every child they had treated, even those whose treatment had been extensive. The study had to rely on fallible procedure such as memory because, with all the limitations, the alternative—a review of the vast number of medical records in the files of the physicians of the county—was an impractical procedure. Similarly, it was not practical to examine the millions of records at Duke Medical Center in order to cull from these files the residents of Alamance County. Even on high speed sorters this would have been impossible. Moreover, there is reason to believe that most of the records at Duke Medical Center would have been duplications of other medical records. Furthermore, it was not necessary to contact every agency: the Epileptic Colony of North Carolina, for example, serves the epileptic children of Alamance County and admission to that facility is arranged through the Welfare Department, which has these records. Individual cases may have been deliberately concealed for one reason or another or missed in this review due to filing procedures, but there is no reason to believe that any systematic bias exists in the collection of these agency materials. In sum, the medical records review provides, subject to the aforementioned limitations, a picture of the totality of medical records existent for children of the county related to the categories of handicapping conditions being studied.

Some additional comments concerning information in files are relevant here. All agencies do not report every child served by or known to the agency. The Welfare Department, for example, may know of a child who is reportedly handicapped but, since service from the Welfare Department has never been requested, no medical record on the child is maintained at that department. Again, an agency which provides no service for mental retardates may be aware that a child receiving other services is mentally retarded without recording the fact in its files. All agencies serving children in the county tend toward some focus or foci of care, and this introduces bias into every agency's files, as will be shown below.

In approaching all agencies dealing with handicapped children, the operational definition of "handicapping condition" was left to the agency itself. Otherwise, the agency would have been forced to revamp its reports to fit what, to that agency, would have seemed an arbitrary set of definitions. For example, the instructions given the Health Department's public health nurses were to list the children known by them to be handicapped. Since the nurses of the Health Department are charged with the responsibility of examining the visual acuity of all school children, 250, or almost 40 per cent of the 526 children reported by the nurses as handicapped, were listed as visually handicapped. Specialized interests such as this not only have consequences for the gathering of data on handicapped children, but, more important, they have implications as to the quality and adequacy of health services. This specialization points up the necessity of providing channels of communication between agencies.

The quantity of reports by agencies is directly influenced by the type of financing of the agency. Public agencies maintain files which are much more thorough than private agencies since they report to state or federal auditors in order to justify expenditures. This budgetary function of medical records has some dysfunctions, however, among which is the inclusion of essentially normal children who have been served for one reason or another.

The quality of reports varies, also, in terms of the training of those making diagnoses. In schools, for example, many diagnoses are based on the judgment of teachers, whose competence is evaluated elsewhere. (See Chapter III.) In the Welfare Department social workers are primarily responsible for many of the diagnoses made, although these workers often have access to medical information forwarded to the Department by interested physicians. Physicians themselves may be expected to vary in the quality of their diagnostic efforts: physicians staffing an orthopedic clinic maintained by state and federal money may have as many as 100 patients to examine in a single day and the diagnoses recorded are necessarily often incomplete with regard to the children's total problems.

Considering these limitations, medical records undoubtedly offer only a specialized perspective of the entire problem. A medical agency assumes that it is not responsible for the overall medical care of the child as the parent is ultimately responsible and the health agencies are only there to help. When such agencies note handicapping conditions which are legally, traditionally, or professionally beyond their interests, they may advise the parent to seek help elsewhere without making a record of the fact. The assumption that a parent is responsible makes such practices possible. Our data show that parents often seek medical assistance from only one source. Combine with this the fact that limited formal communication linkages exist between agencies themselves and the pattern of incompleteness becomes clear. Medical authorities report only those cases (1) which are brought to their attention, (2) which are within their field of specialization and (3) for which care and service are possible.

Thus, the data provided by the medical records review must be viewed as minimal estimates of the total number of medically significant conditions existing in a community. At best they represent a picture of the problems serviced by the majority of health agencies of the county. For some conditions there will be overreporting and for others, underreporting. The figures which result from this examination of medical records are, however, one *kind* of prevalence; they reflect community and formal medical awareness. These estimates indicate what the medical and paramedical workers are doing with their money and their energies. As such, they provide data for answering such questions as, "Is this the way we want our money spent?"

The following health agencies were approached for data by the study's staff: State Department of Public Welfare, State Board of Health, State Commission for the Blind, Board of Correction and

Training, Department of Vocational Rehabilitation, State Hospitals Board of Control, State Schools for the Blind and Deaf, State Cerebral Palsy Hospital, Burlington City and Alamance County Schools, Alamance County Health Department, Alamance County Department of Public Welfare, Alamance County Hospital, Alamance General Hospital, North Carolina Memorial Hospital, the physicians and dentists in private practice in the county, and various private charities.

The procedure involved in securing the desired information from the school system of Alamance County is of particular interest because it illustrates the steps involved in working with the sources of information. Conferences were initially held with the State Superintendent of Public Instruction and the State Director of Special Education and their approval of the project secured. Contacts were then made with the superintendents of the two school systems and, with their approval, the school survey was broached to conferences of the school principals. Through the principals, the survey form used in the school survey was distributed to the individual teachers. The teachers completed the forms and returned them to the study staff. In all cases, the procedure described above was followed: permission was secured at the state level first and only then were local contacts made.

Early in the study it was recognized that the information in files would be maintained and catalogued differently—that the files would vary in completeness and currency since they reflect the purposes, interests, legal responsibilities, special needs, and historical accidents of the agencies studied. The form used was designed to standardize the information elicited from each agency. Whenever possible, the entire form was completed; where omissions occurred in the files themselves, no attempt at cross checking to other referrals was made. Thus, the data contain a rather clear picture of the kind of information maintained in various files of the county.

Private physicians and dentists presented special problems for the gathering of data. In approaching them the staff presented before county medical and dental societies a brief statement of the aims and intentions of the study and requested endorsement from those groups. In both cases approval was given. Following these meetings, a letter was sent to the individual physicians and dentists requesting that they list all handicapped children known to them. A stamped, self-addressed envelop was enclosed for return. It had been planned to return to the physician's office and complete the standard form used in this study after the list of names had been returned. Only a few physicians and dentists, however, returned the names. It was found necessary to make a series of telephone calls and personal visits before the busy practitioners could be induced to complete the list of handicapped children known to them. The tremendous efforts involved in gathering these data were, as it turned out, not worth-while. Only 319 children were reported as handicapped by physicians, that is, only eight per cent of the total reported by all medical and para-medical agencies in the county. One-half of the total number of handicapped children reported by all physicians were known to and reported by three pediatricians.

Public agencies were contacted between October, 1961, and February, 1962. Only reports from the public agencies were included in sampling rosters for invitation to the clinic of April, 1962, so as to eliminate any possible violation of professional confidentiality. The survey of all medical agencies was completed by November, 1962.

Presented in Table 1 are the prevalence estimates of the several conditions derived from the agency data for both public and private agencies.

TABLE 1

Prevalence Rates of Handicapping Conditions Per 1000 Persons
Under 21 by Sex and Race, Agency Data

Condition	Total	Male	Female	White	Negro
Orthopedic conditions	16	13	14	17	13
Epilepsy	2	3	1	2	2
Vision defects	14	15	14	15	9
Hearing defects	3	4	3	3	2
Cleft palate	1	2	1	2	1
Emotional disturbance	19	25	14	22	12
Speech disorders	16	22	10	15	22
Mental retardation:	28	38	18	27	31
Presumptive	(14)				
Educable	(12)				
Trainable	(1)				
Custodial	(1)				
Respiratory disorders	8	9	7	8	8
Heart conditions	5	5	6	5	6
Orthodontic conditions	2	2	2	2	1
Cerebral palsy	2	2	2	2	1
Skin conditions	2	2	1	1	4
Other		20	16	17	21
Numbers in population		18,600	17,900	29,000	7,400

The assumptions underlying the construction of the agency rates are that the reports obtained include all of the medical records of Alamance County and that the total population, where appropriate, can be used as a base for constructing these rates. Table 1 is con-structed using these assumptions. It should be noted, however, that these are not true for the reports from individual agencies: there is really no way of estimating the population served by a particular agency, the one exception being the schools. The agencies of the county contained records on 4,083 children, which constitutes eleven per cent of the population under 21 years of age. There were 5,953 different reports, an average of 1.46 reports per child, indicating that most of the children are reported by one agency only. A total of 7,382 specific diagnoses were made in these reports.

Considering agency reports alone, the most frequently reported condition is that of mental retardation, which affects almost three per cent of the county's population under 21 years of age. This figure, while agreeing with previous estimates of mental retardation,[5] must be considered low because it is conditioned by parental and agency acknowledgment of mental retardation. Large numbers of children are reported to be emotionally disturbed (about 2 per cent), orthopedically disabled (about 1.6 per cent), and as having vision defects (about 1.4 per cent). Considering sheer numbers of people, the greatest needs, as indicated by these reports, are in the areas of mental health, orthopedics, and vision, areas being serviced, as we shall see, by large service agencies.

An important qualification is to be noted in the area of mental retardation with regard to these agency reports: in cases where the agency files could not provide an Intelligence Quotient, or a reasonable approximation of the severity of the limitation involved, the classification of "presumptive retardation" was used. In other words, many of the presumptively mentally retarded had been examined psychologically but the agency knew only that the child was retarded— or guessed that the child was retarded—and could not categorize him as educable, trainable, or custodial. These figures do not suggest that as many retardates are untested as have been tested; at the same time they do indicate a need for additional psychological service in the county.

The data in columns 2, 3, 4 and 5 of Table 1 show that, in general, more males than females and more whites than Negroes are reported by the health agencies of the county. The observed differences by sex are notable. The percentage of males in the population base is 51 per cent while 61 per cent of the agencies' reports concerned males. More males are reported as handicapped for both whites and Negroes. This finding is unexpected since there are no medical reasons to believe that most handicapping conditions are sex-related. It suggests that assistance may be sought by parents more

5. The President's Panel on Mental Retardation, A Proposed Program for National Action to Combat Mental Retardation. (Washington, D. C.): Government Printing Office (1962), p. 1.

frequently for boys than for girls, probably as a result of the differential expectations for males in our society. This sex bias in medical reports may indicate that females are not receiving the medical attention accorded males.

On the whole, Negro children are reported as handicapped less frequently than are white children. This is an unexpected finding since the socio-economic conditions of Negroes generally might be expected to generate health needs.

TABLE 2

Percentage Distribution of Reports by Sex and Race
for the Largest Reporting Agencies of the County

Agency	% Male	% Negro	Numbers
Health Department	54	16	999
Welfare Department	60	20	923
Schools	68	26	922
Hospitals	58	12	757
State Board of Health	55	18	565
All Physicians	57	8	319
In the population under 21	51	20	

As shown in Table 2 all agencies report a greater proportion of males than their proportion of the population. All but two agencies, the Welfare Department and the schools, report fewer Negro children than would be expected on the basis of population distribution, and only one, the schools, reports a greater number of Negro children than their proportion of the population. The private agencies, i.e., hospitals and practicing physicians, report a particularly low percentage of Negro children, and this probably accounts for a major part of the racial disparity revealed in Table 1.

A further step in analyzing the data from agencies is the examination of the percentage distributions of diagnostic reports within each agency. These data are presented in Table 3. For comparative purposes the last column gives the percentage distribution of handicapping conditions with moderate or severe disability as estimated from the clinical examinations.

The data in Table 3 permit judgments as to the foci of interests or the extent of specialization within each agency. Thus, these data indicate that a preponderance of Health Department reports are for orthopedic conditions, vision, and emotional problems: the high rate of orthopedic referrals is related to the department's participation in the orthopedic clinics maintained by the State Board of Health, from which come the records in its orthopedic files. The emphasis on vision problems grows out of the public health nurses' responsibility for checking the visual acuity of all school children in the county.

TABLE 3

Percentage Distribution of Diagnoses Reported by the Largest Reporting Agencies of Alamance County

Condition	Health Dept.	Welfare¹ Dept.	Board of Health	Hospitals Control	All Schools	Private Physicians	All Hospitals	Expected² Distribution
Orthopedic conditions	21	2	32	7	12	19	16	5
Epilepsy	1	1	...	1	2	4	2	4
Vision defects	22	4	1	9	3	6	14	9
Hearing defects	2	1	2	1	3	2	2	3
Cleft palate	2	1	2	1	1	3	...	1
Emotional disturbance	10	22	27	6	12	4	23	18
Speech disorders	4	1	1	5	29	3	1	4
Mental retardation:	8	30	1	53	36	13	6	27
Presumptive	(6)	(25)	(1)	(7)	(11)	(12)	(4)	
Educable	(2)	(4)		(19)	(22)			
Trainable				(14)	(3)		(1)	
Custodial				(13)		(1)	(1)	
Respiratory disorders			3	3	1		10	10
Heart conditions	2	1	6	2		17	10	1
Orthodontic conditions	7		1	2		17		12
Cerebral palsy	1		3	5	1	7	1	2
Skin conditions	4	1	3			1	1	4
Other	14	34	17	5	2	3	12	
TOTAL	100	100	100	100	100	100	100	100
N of diagnoses	1,192	1,120	598	140	1,294	504	878	12,150
N of children	999	923	565	76	922	319	757	7,147

1. The Welfare Department's records as reported here are based on Individual Children's Cards rather than on the total records maintained by the department. As a result, the percentage of "other" conditions and "presumptive" retardates is quite high.

2. This distribution is based on the clinic adjusted estimates of the moderate and severe conditions only. See text.

Similarly, this department maintains the records of a privately supported clinical psychologist who works at the department one day a week. This psychologist serves the young of the county by diagnostic work only and does not offer any other service.

The areas of concentration of the Welfare Department are those of emotional disturbance and mental retardation. In this, the department is servicing the major problem areas of the county. The services of the Welfare Department in these areas are multiple: the department is legally responsible for the processing of all applications to special state schools, such as the schools for the mentally retarded. Administering psychological examinations to those recommended for special education classes in the local school systems is another major task of the Welfare Department. Also, the department provides services to the socio-economically deprived families in Alamance County, families in which a high prevalence of emotional disturbance and, presumably, mental retardation might be expected.

The foci of interests of the State Board of Health are in the areas of orthopedic conditions and emotional disturbance. Both interests are the result of the Board's responsibility for the orthopedic clinics and the mental health clinics of the state.

The Hospitals Board of Control* maintains the State Training Schools for Mentally Retarded Children; the other diagnoses listed in their reports reflect the additional medical care provided for the institutionalized child.

School teachers are particularly concerned with the areas of mental retardation, speech, emotional disturbance, and orthopedic conditions.

Physicians in private practice are frequently consulted on orthopedic and chronic respiratory conditions. They recognize mental retardation, although they offer little service for this condition.

Emotional disturbance, orthopedic conditions, and visual problems are heavily represented in the records of the hospitals serving the county.

A comparison of the percentage distribution within each agency with the percentage distribution of moderate and severe conditions derived from the clinic phase of the study reveals that each agency has a rather low recognition rate for problems outside its areas of special interest. There is, therefore, no agency or combination of agencies, except the aggregate of them all, through whose records a

---

* After the study was completed this agency's name was changed to Department of Mental Health.

representative distribution of handicapping conditions may be gathered.

There is an almost inverse relationship between the ease of data gathering and the number of children reported. The physicians of the county, for example, reported 319 children as handicapped, yet their records, involving much personal contact and visits, were the most difficult to obtain. Generally speaking, the public agencies of the county maintained their records in such a manner as to make processing relatively easy.

There are other agencies in Alamance County which are not included in Table 3. This omission is permissible in that: (1) some of the agencies report so few children that there might be some danger of violating confidentiality of the medical records; (2) as the number of reports decreases, medical specialization becomes even more pronounced; (3) the additional information would not increase the observations made concerning these data.

As pointed out earlier, the definitions of handicapped children and handicapping conditions vary from agency to agency and thus the data contained in these tables must be interpreted cautiously. Even with the vagaries of definition unresolved, there are some general propositions which may be advanced concerning these agency data. First, 11 per cent of the population under 21 years of age is defined as handicapped by the medical and paramedical agencies of the county. Second, the prevalence rates generated by the examination of medical records is biased in terms of the medical or special interests of that agency as well as by the race and sex of the children defined as handicapped. Third, no single agency provides an adequate estimate of the total needs of the county in terms either of the number of children or their handicaps as demonstrated by the clinical examination phase of the study. Fourth, as will be demonstrated below, the agency reports provide the most conservative of the prevalence estimates obtained by the three methods used in this study.

The Household Survey

The second phase of the research activity of the study concerned the gathering of morbidity data by means of a five per cent sample survey of the households in Alamance County. It was anticipated that this survey would generate different estimates of the prevalence of handicapping conditions but the differences, reported in Table 6, were larger than expected.

A specially designed questionnaire was developed by the staff to measure the prevalence of conditions regardless of severity, prior treatment, or professional diagnoses. The study staff was interested in collecting data on parental awareness and concern rather than treatment. Thus, the definition of a handicapped child for the survey might be said to be the existence of some degree of parental concern. Children were classified by condition in terms of positive responses to questions which covered various areas of concern.

The questionnaire used was straightforward and designed for administration by lay canvassers. The decision to use lay volunteers as canvassers was based on considerations of cost as well as a belief that they could do the job adequately. If this belief proved to be correct, it would be possible to recommend similar studies by other communities at nominal expense. Our data indicate that lay workers, with some training and a well designed questionnaire, can do the job adequately. (See Chapter VI.)

Fifty-eight volunteer workers, eight nurses, eight social workers, and five professional interviewers completed interviews of 1,032 households in randomly assigned areas of the county. These interviews were completed during the period of 1 March through 17 March, 1962. Completed questionnaires were returned on 1,864 children—approximately 4.6 per cent of the estimated population of the county. There was no evidence that any systematic bias existed in the collection of these statistics.

The rates of handicapping conditions reported for the household survey are presented in Table 4. Included are breakdowns in terms of age, sex, race, and social class.

The data in Table 4 may be interpreted in several ways. First, over fifty per cent of the parents interviewed considered their children to be "handicapped," in terms of the definition cited above. Second, the relative order of handicapping conditions is not the same as for the agency data: parents are concerned about chronic skin conditions, chronic respiratory conditions, and visual difficulties. Third, there is a relatively consistent increase with age in the number of children reported as handicapped. Fourth, more males are reported overall, as handicapped than females. Fifth, more Negro children are reported as handicapped than white. Sixth, more families judged by the interviewers to be of the "lower class" reported their children to be handicapped than the upper, middle, or working class. Seventh, almost one fifth of the total number of reported handicapped children

TABLE 4

Prevalence Rates of Presumptively Handicapping Conditions Per 1,000 Persons Under 21 by Selected Social and Demographic Characteristics, Survey Data

Presumptive Diagnosis	Total Sample	Age				Sex		Race		Social Class		
		0-4	5-9	10-14	15-20	Male	Female	White	Negro	Upper & Middle	Working	Lower
Any handicap	508	373	506	565	605	525	490	500	546	503	479	602
Orthopedic conditions	63	39	42	70	109	68	59	64	60	64	58	83
Epilepsy	31	23	24	45	31	36	26	33	27	15	33	37
Vision defects	126	25	76	203	221	109	143	121	147	132	118	141
Hearing defects	30	2	38	50	25	40	20	26	48	22	28	43
Cleft palate	1	0	2	0	0	1	0	0	0	0	0	2
Emotional disturbance	30	16	42	35	23	32	27	24	54	11	22	63
Speech disorders	64	32	99	85	40	85	42	55	87	60	43	123
Mental retardation	79	48	81	97	89	100	59	65	141	34	60	172
Respiratory disorders	163	126	162	158	213	181	145	148	225	170	148	207
Heart conditions	27	6	31	22	54	23	32	27	30	11	31	31
Orthodontic conditions	35	0	58	42	46	18	53	30	57	37	29	54
Cerebral palsy	5	0	9	5	8	9	1	6	3	3	5	5
Skin conditions	148	131	126	160	178	141	156	133	213	128	143	175
Other	105	112	113	90	109	101	109	108	84	136	105	86

are classified as having conditions not classified in the 13 categories of handicapping conditions studied here.

The differences in reported rates of handicapping conditions by age, sex, race, and class are interesting in terms of the source of report. One caution is necessary, however, before proceeding: it is not expected that parental concern can be validated by health records; health records measure services sought while questionnaires measure something quite different, namely parental concern based on the parent-child relationship. A parent may define himself as a "good parent" when he or she feels concerned about the health of the child. The logical validity of the questions used was such that it was not expected that parents would describe minor symptoms as significant, yet these data indicate that all degrees of condition, not just those actually causing some measure of handicap, are included by parents in their responses. The most interesting phenomenon of all, however, is that some clinical validation of a high proportion of these conditions was possible.

Regarding sex differences in reports, parents report more males as handicapped than females. It is probable that here, as in the agency reports, differential expectations for males serve to increase the probability of recognizing medically significant problems. More females than males, however, are reported by their parents to suffer from skin, heart, and visual defects, reflecting possibly, for the skin and vision defects at least, the social expectations of the female.

Regarding age, the parents of the county perceive more orthopedic, visual, respiratory and skin conditions with increase in age. Mental retardation, however, increases to a maximum and then decreases with age; this phenomenon is consistent with other reports.[6] Recognition of other difficulties appears to reach a maximum in the five to ten year age category: emotional disturbance, speech disorder, orthodontic difficulty and cerebral palsy. It is probable that during this age period parents experience their first opportunity to compare their child's performances with his peers outside the home.

Differential rates of handicapping conditions by race provide some provocative data for analysis. Some of the differences reported for Negro and white children in the survey are in the opposite direction than those reported by the agencies of the county. White children, for example, were reported by the agencies to suffer emotional problems more often than Negro children, yet twice as

6. Melvin B. Goodman, Ernest M. Gruenberg, Joseph J. Downing and Eugene Rogot, "A Prevalence Study of Mental Retardation in a Metropolitan Area," *American Journal of Public Health* 46 (June, 1956), pp. 702-707.

many Negro parents as white parents are concerned about the emotional stability of their children. Similarly, the reported rate of mental retardation for Negro children from the survey is more than twice the rate reported for white children, yet the agency rates, reported in Table 1, indicate no difference by race but a difference by sex. Chronic respiratory conditions are of great concern to Negro parents yet, again, the agency data indicates almost no difference by race. One can conclude from these data that Negro parents recognize more signs of handicapping conditions among their children than do white parents but they do not, for one reason or another, receive as much medical attention for them.

Comparisons between agency and survey data by social class are, at present, impossible as the agency data are only partially complete with regard to entries of social class. The survey data alone, however, indicate some notable disparities between diagnoses by social class: five times as many lower class families, for example, report their children to be emotionally disturbed as do the parents of upper or middle class families. It is probable that these observed differences are due to the fact that lower class parents worry more about their children yet do less for them than parents of other social strata. This may indicate that an important role for the medical agencies is one of reassuring parents about behavior aberrations exhibited by their children which are not medically significant. It is probable also, that these differences reflect some real differences among social classes. The lower classes probably receive poorer care, less health assistance, and less education, all of which could be reflected in the parental concern reported here.

It has been shown here that various social factors are related to the reporting of medical conditions in a health survey. These factors must be taken into consideration when evaluating data generated by health surveys. Some of the observed differences are probably due to real differences between age categories, the sexes, the races, and social classes but some additional portion is due to factors other than real differences in health. The issues involved in attributing observed differences to "real" differences and to problems of measurement are too complex to be resolved at this stage of research. It appears, however, that using agency-generated data as a satisfactory criterion of health would be a questionable procedure. It may be noted at this point that simple overreporting and underreporting by parents does not invalidate the utility of the questionnaire approach to the understanding of health problems since fully seventy-five per cent of the conditions reported by the parents could be confirmed by clinical examination. This verification of conditions reported obtained despite the relatively rigid categories of diagnoses which were used and also the relatively transient nature of some of the conditions being studied. On the other hand, of the 87 presumptively normal children examined in the clinic phase of the study, thirty-two per cent were found to suffer from some significant or potentially significant condition.

Clinical Examinations

One major purpose of the clinical examination phase of the study was to validate the reports made to the staff by either the health agencies or by the household survey, as well as to substantiate the presumptive diagnosis on the basis of which the child was invited to the clinic. Other purposes were: (1) to determine what other conditions, if any, the patient exhibited; (2) to estimate the severity of the condition affecting the child, and (3) to suggest a course of action to help the child. In this last purpose, of course, the staff was concerned with estimating the medical and paramedical services required of the county.

Fifty-two clinic sessions were held in Alamance County Hospital, Burlington, North Carolina. These sessions of three hours each were held during the mornings and afternoons of twenty-six working days in April, May and August, 1962. To this clinic were invited 700 presumptively normal and handicapped children; 456, or 65 per cent, attended and were examined.

The children invited to the clinic included presumptively normal children in order to provide some estimate of the extent of under-reporting on the health questionnaire and the reports of the medical agencies of the county. These normal children were, in effect, the "control" subjects concerning whom no services were reportedly needed.

Of the 456 children who attended the clinic, 299, or 66 per cent, were invited through the survey reports and 157 were children reported by the health agencies. Invitations were based on a random sample drawn by the "primary" diagnostic conditions. For the agency referrals, this listing was based on the agency reports; for the survey reports, a more or less arbitrary list of conditions was constructed so that children with multiple conditions would appear only once in the entire listing. This procedure permitted the children to be invited to clinics where specialists for certain conditions could be present. It meant, however, that some children were examined at the clinic more than one time if the examining physician at the first clinic believed consultation with other specialists would be helpful.

Sample size for each condition was contingent upon: (1) the number of cases reported; (2) the operational requirements of the clinic itself, and (3) the minimum number required to provide a reasonable degree of reliability of the sample. These samples varied from the total number of cerebral palsy cases reported in the survey to one in seven of the presumptively normal children. No attempt was made to stratify these subsamples in terms of age, race, sex, or social class.

The basic staff of each clinic comprised a psychologist, a pediatrician, social workers, nurses, and five volunteer workers. The medical director of the project acted as supervisor for all clinic sessions. Specialists in each area of disability were added to this basic staff as needed: these represented all medical specialties with which the study dealt. For the clinic sessions dealing with cerebral palsy, there were 28 staff members for the examination of 18 children. The volunteer workers assisted the pediatrician by recording his dictated notes, by aiding the psychologist in administering the Draw-a-Man test and the California Personality Inventory, and dressing and undressing the young children. They were very helpful also in administering the vision and hearing checks and in entertaining the children during the periods of inactivity.

The clinic opened with four days of examination of presumptively normal children. These control subjects were invited first because it was felt that it would be easier to get the routine established with these "normals" and because referrals to later clinics could be made whenever the examining physicians deemed such referrals necessary. On these normal days, 44 children were invited to the clinic, twenty-two in the morning and twenty-two in the afternoon. Previous research and professional experience lead the staff to believe that not all of the invitees would attend; it was hoped that eighteen children would attend each session.

Letters of invitation to the clinic were sent to each home one week prior to the day the child was expected at the clinic. A stamped, self-addressed post card was to be returned by the parents of the invitee if they planned to attend. No more than half of the persons examined returned these cards. It was constantly necessary to make either telephone calls or personal contacts with the invitees. Such contacts made it possible for the staff to determine the kinds of non-participation involved and served as well to motivate doubters to attend the clinic.

The staff did everything in its power to encourage attendance. Baby sitting services, transportation to and from the clinic, contacts with schools and employers were just some of the services which were offered. In addition, local medical and paramedical agencies were contacted in attempts to encourage participation.

The procedures employed in the clinic were straightforward. Completed for every child were: a medical history, a social history, a screening of vision and hearing, a screening examination for mental retardation and emotional disturbance, and a pediatric examination. For the presumptively handicapped children relevant examinations were added. On days when cleft palate children were examined, for example, a plastic surgeon, a speech therapist, and a otolaryngologist were added to the basic clinic staff.

The sequence of interviews and examinations was not fixed. It would have been desirable to have the psychologist examine the children before they had been upset by the physician's examination, but this was not always possible. The only requirement imposed was that the medical history be completed before the pediatrician examined the child. In all other stages of the clinic, patients were routed as an examiner was available. This necessitated the constant presence of a traffic supervisor, but it reduced the total time spent in the clinic by each patient.

The constant attendance of the supervisor, usually the medical director of the project, made it possible for him to speak to each parent whose child had been examined. This saved the task of making a report of the examination by mail to each child's family. In cases where the parent could not wait or where the child came in without his parents, a letter was sent to the parents or guardian of the child describing the results of his examination.

Following each clinic session, a staff conference concerning each child was held. Here the entire staff participated in making judgments concerning the validation of presumptive diagnoses, ancillary conditions and severity of disabilities, and in outlining a program of care for the child. In these sessions the goal was the care of the "whole child" and all recommendations were considered in the light of the family situation in which the child lived. These conferences never proved dull since they included facets of medicine, sociology, law, ethics, and philosophy. While they were interesting, they were not uniformly productive either. Some sessions ended with the staff at a complete standstill as to what to do with this or that particular case. It is most significant that even with the most knowledgeable people in the community assembled around a conference table and with the resources of the community at their disposal, it was extremely difficult to arrive at a definitive statement concerning the "ought to be" for every child. Persons in their uniqueness, are just too complex for the situation to be otherwise. The group learned that all too often the legal restrictions imposed on service agencies prevented service or care to individuals who did not meet specific medical or legal definitions or whose problems did not fall within the limited responsibilities of the agency involved.

Expenses at the clinic were minimal. Clinic facilities were provided by the hospital at cost as a community enterprise and the total costs including examining rooms, laboratory procedures, and even meals for the entire staff, were less than a dollar per patient.

TABLE 5

Clinically Adjusted Rates of Handicapping Conditions Per 1,000 Persons Under 21 and Percentage Distributions of Estimated Severity for Each Diagnosis, Alamance County

Condition	Adjusted Clinical Rates	Percentage Distribution of Severity For Each Diagnosis				Rates For Moderate & Severe
		None	Mild	Moderate	Severe	
Orthopedic conditions	60	17	61	17	6	13
Epilepsy	12	....	....	100	....	12
Vision defects	123	54	24	16	6	27
Hearing defects	49	24	57	19	....	9
Cleft palate	3	50	....	....	50	2
Emotional disturbance	106	....	51	38	11	52
Speech disorders	46	3	71	19	6	12
Mental retardation:	90	....	15	55	30	77
Presumptive	(8)	....	(50)	(50)	....	....
Educable	(70)	....	(13)	(67)	(20)	....
Trainable	(9)	....	....	....	(100)	....
Custodial	(2)	....	....	....	(100)	....
Respiratory disorders	103	4	65	21	7	29
Heart conditions	63	77	17	3	3	4
Orthodontic conditions	89	....	60	37	3	37
Cerebral palsy	8	....	20	60	20	6
Skin conditions	77	14	71	14	....	11

Presented in Table 5 are the clinic adjusted estimates of handicapping conditions with the percentage distributions of estimated severity as judged by the staff conferences held after each clinic session. The adjustment procedure employed here is simply a weighting of the survey rates, on the basis of which 66 per cent of these children were invited, to account for the over- and underreporting of conditions. For example, the household survey data indicated that there were 804 normal children in the five per cent sample of the county. Of these, 87 children were examined in the clinic. Fifty-nine of those examined were found to be normal. The best estimate of the total number of normal children in the household survey sample would then be 59/87 times 804. This procedure assumes that the normal children who attended and those who did not attend were of the same medical condition. For the total normal population, added to these 59 normal children were all those children who were presumably handicapped but who were found to be normal upon examination. The sampling rates being different for each diagnostic subsample, the weights change within each sample. The figures in the first column of Table 5, then, are adjusted to include all cases of underreporting and overreporting for each diagnostic category.

These adjusted clinical rates were higher than expected, and far higher than rates reported by other studies. Validation of presumptive conditions from the survey questionnaire was recorded if any basis was found for a positive response to a question—e.g., a functional heart murmur was "validation" of parental concern. This procedure may be open to question, but such patients need understanding and reassurance as much as children with rheumatic fever need penicillin prophylaxis. Our procedure resulted in a high percentage of conditions being recorded which caused no disability or only mild disability, as shown in the other columns of Table 5. In addition to this, however, there is reason to believe that, with the wholehearted interest and participation of the community, we may have succeeded in getting a more nearly complete picture of existing handicapping problems than some previous studies.

From the standpoint of need for services and facilities, the rates for conditions which cause moderate to severe disability, as shown in the last column, provide the best and most significant estimates. Also, these appear to be somewhat more comparable to estimates from other sources. Considering only these moderate to severe conditions, the important problems are mental retardation, emotional disturbance, orthodontic problems, chronic respiratory conditions, and visual difficulties.

The significance of these data may be grasped more fully by suggesting that there are 2,800 mentally retarded children living in Alamance County. It is also estimated that there are 1,900 children with moderate to severe emotional problems. Orthodontic problems rank third in terms of the number of children affected, with an estimated 1,300 children involved. Chronic respiratory conditions affect an additional 1,050 children; an equal number suffer from a moderately to severely handicapping visual problem.

It is of interest to compare the prevalence rates from the three steps of the present study with those from Wishik's Georgia study. These are brought together in Table 6. The Georgia study employed procedures very similar to the survey and clinical evaluations in Alamance County except that no presumably normal children were examined.

TABLE 6

Comparison of Rates of Handicapping Conditions Per 1,000
Persons Under 21 by Source of Information

| Condition | Alamance County | | | |
	Agency Reports	Household Survey	Clinic Examinations[1]	Wishik[2]
Orthopedic conditions	16	63	13	15
Epilepsy	2	31	12	4
Vision defects	14	126	27	23
Hearing defects	3	30	9	19
Cleft palate	1	1	2	18
Emotional disturbance	19	30	52	26
Speech disorders	16	64	12	27
Mental retardation	28	79	77	37
Respiratory disorders	8	163	29	*
Heart conditions	5	27	4	9
Orthodontic conditions	2	35	36	15
Cerebral palsy	2	5	6	5
Skin conditions	2	148	11	*

* No data available.
1. Moderate and severe only.
2. See footnote to Chapter I, re: Wishik.

Some of the differences between the rates derived from the agency data, the household survey, and the clinical examinations have already been discussed. Services available, seriousness of problem and special emphases are doubtless reflected in both the agency and the household survey rates. For example, an active crippled children's program is reflected in the rates of orthopedic conditions in both.

The highest rates in the household survey were for chronic respiratory conditions and chronic skin conditions, both of which are quite obvious to parents, and are likely, because of their obviousness, to create parental concern out of proportion to their significance. Mental retardation has the highest rates in both our agency and clinic data and in Wishik's data. Personality and emotional difficulties rank second in the agency and clinic examination data, and are nosed out of second place in Wishik's data by speech defects by only a single point. The area of mental and emotional problems is by a considerable margin the largest problem as shown by the two columns which are believed to represent the closest approximation to true prevalence, our clinic examination rates and Wishik's rates.

It is interesting that for three conditions agency rates exceed those from the clinic examinations: orthopedic conditions, speech defects and heart conditions. There are doubtless several factors which account for this phenomenon, but community emphasis and available services must play a part.

Particularly striking is the low prevalence in the agency data of orthodontic conditions compared with the data in the other series. There was no orthodontist in the county at the time of the study, and there was a strong impression that such conditions were simply accepted and were not culturally defined as "handicapped."

Between our clinical examination data and Wishik's there are some differences for which reasons are not readily apparent. Some probably relate to the specific criteria employed or to differences in interpretation of these criteria by the examining physicians. Others probably relate to the correction of our rates on the basis of the findings in the presumably normal children who were examined. It is noteworthy, however, that although the Alamance rates are generally higher, the rank orders are not too dissimilar. His rates are higher than ours for orthopedic conditions, hearing problems, cleft palate, speech problems and heart conditions. Ours are higher than his for the other six conditions represented in both, but the difference is marked only for epilepsy, emotional problems, mental retardation and orthodontic conditions.

A Note on Seriousness of Condition

For Alamance County three estimates of prevalence rates have been presented. The estimate on the basis of the agency review suggests a rate of handicapping of 11 per cent of the population under 21; the survey data provide an estimate of roughly 50 per cent; the estimate from the clinic examinations (based on children invited from the survey), is 43 per cent potentially handicapped and 20 per cent with moderate to severe handicapping. It is evident from this latter figure that both the survey rate and the total clinic rate included a very large number of relatively unimportant conditions.

There was no rating of the children in agency records by severity, but the question arises whether the 11 per cent of the children of the county represented in these records were the more severe cases, those who came for help because they were in greater need of service. This did not prove to be the case. Thirty-seven per cent of the handicapping conditions found among the 157 agency children examined in the clinic were classified as moderate or severe, only two percentage points higher than the 35 per cent for all children in the county as estimated from the examination of survey children.

Another comparison between the agency and survey populations is found in Table 7, which shows the percentage of children examined from the two sources who were judged to have no vocational limitation, some limitation or total restrictions. These estimates were made by the conferees after each session in an attempt to answer the question, "Can this child, given optimum medical care and training, be expected to be gainfully employed during his lifetime?"

TABLE 7

Comparison of the Estimates of Vocational Handicaps for
Agency and Survey Children Examined in the Clinic

Type of Limitation	Percentage of Children	
	Agency Invitees	Survey Invitees
Not handicapped	57	78
Physical limitation	13	12
Mental limitation	13	4
Social limitation	13	4
Total restriction	5	3

The percentage of agency children with total restriction, 5 per cent, is higher than the 3 per cent of survey children so classified. The 56 per cent of agency children with no vocational limitation, although lower than the 78 per cent of survey children not limited, is still quite high. These high percentages in both groups reflect in part the fact that many of the conditions reported and in need of treatment are not vocationally limiting. In part, they also reflect significant overreporting for both groups.

It is, after all, not surprising that agency reports should include a large number of non-handicapped children. They represent, in the main, those who have sought rather than those who need help, and there is a difference. One exception is the children who are reported from the schools based on the teachers' knowledge or judgment regarding conditions existing in their pupils. Another interesting note with reference to severity of condition is that the number of conditions per child increases with the severity of the primary diagnosis. This is shown in Table 8. Primary diagnosis as used here is the condition judged by the examining physician to be the most important one. The conclusion is clear that the greater the medical significance of the primary condition, the greater the likelihood of there being some other condition present. Of course, some of these other conditions are related to the primary condition, but interrelatedness was not specifically evaluated because it was not germaine to the need for services.

TABLE 8

The Average Number of Handicapping Conditions Per Handicapped Child
By Severity of Primary Diagnosis

Severity of Primary Diagnosis	Average Number of Conditions
None	1
Mild	1
Moderate	2
Severe	3
Total Group	1.60

Note: Number of Children = 456.

Summary

The following points may be made concerning the handicapped children of Alamance County:

1) The prevalence of handicapping conditions in children in Alamance County is enormous with approximately 20 per cent of the population under 21 years of age affected.
2) The greatest problems in the county are in the areas of mental health; seven per cent of the county's youth may be described as mentally retarded and 5 per cent as emotionally disturbed.
3) The majority of the handicapped children are not known to the medical agencies of the county and are not receiving needed care.
4) The handicapped children of the county are not taking full advantage of the medical and service facilities already available in the county.
5) The specialization, both of medical practitioners and of service agencies, tends to be dysfunctional in providing optimum medical care; there is a need for developing channels of communication between health agencies.
6) Different techniques of estimating prevalence rates provide different estimates. The smallest rates were found by means of records review; the largest rates were found by a household survey. Apparently these techniques measure different discrete phenomena.
7) For both agency reports and the household survey, more males are reported as handicapped than females; more whites are reported as being serviced than Negroes, but more Negro parents indicate concern over possible handicapping conditions.

8) Non-white, lower class persons are more in need of medical assistance but appear less frequently in the medical records than their numbers lead one to expect.

9) A program of medical education for both the general public and the medical facilities is needed in certain areas of health, as is evidenced by the wide disparities between clinic figures and agency figures, especially in the areas of orthodonture, epilepsy, mental retardation, and emotional disturbance.

10) It is possible for communities to carry out household surveys such as reported here at relatively nominal expenses provided the community itself can be aroused to participate.

The problems which have come to light through the Alamance County experience seem to indicate that the solutions to health problems do not mean simply more physicians, more health workers, more teachers, and so on. Of course, it is necessary to have adequate numbers of medical workers, but the need for capable and responsible people to bring handicapped children to the attention of medical authorities and to follow the advice of the medical authorities is just as important. The community must learn to take advantage of the services which are offered. This suggests that health education must be recognized as a major need in the community.

THE RECORDS REVIEW

THIS SECTION focuses on data relating to possible handicapping conditions available in the records of all the agencies, local and state, serving the children of Alamance County. Although there were some exceptions to complete coverage, we feel that a clear pattern emerges. Our data indicate that medical records seriously underestimate the total morbidity of Alamance County's children. Further, interrelationships are inadequate to compensate for the marked specialization of interests of health agencies in the county, and this "communication problem" has consequences for the kinds of care afforded to the children. Finally, within single health agencies there are many factors which affect the quantity and quality of the health records.

PART II

Three articles are presented in this section. In the first we examine a single agency, the schools, and seek to understand some of the factors which generate health records. In the second paper, the totality of the records is studied and comparisons between public and private agencies noted. The third paper concentrates on the linkages between health agencies, using as an index of communication the referral patterns which ideally bind health agencies together.

There is a social structure within which these health agencies operate. This structure has consequences on the provision of care. It reflects the social relationships which have formed through time, as well as the cultural folkways of the county. If change is desired there must be understanding of the way things are done.

CHAPTER III

AN EVALUATION OF SCHOOL TEACHERS AS SOURCES OF INFORMATION

In studying sources of information concerning morbidity in persons under twenty-one years of age, a special survey of all school teachers in Alamance County was conducted in the winter of 1961-1962. School teachers were included as sources of information because of their exposure to a large number of children and because of their expected competence in recognizing disability in children.

School teachers are in the rather unenviable position of being a source of information concerning children's morbidity because of their exposure to children. It is known that they lack the medical sophistication required of diagnosticians but their close contacts make them available. Coupled with this is the idea that their normal school functions include many which are related to health affairs: they teach the rudiments of health, they are often the instigators of parental concern for the child, and they are expected to call the attention of the health nurse to significant medical conditions affecting children.

The various functions of the teacher in this area make it important that there exist some estimate of the school teachers' performance. There is probably a high correlation between the performance in one of these areas of function and the others, but even if there is no such relationship, estimating the reliability of the school teachers in recognizing medically significant problems may provide insight into the kinds of areas in which teachers need further training.

Estimating the morbidity in a population can be a very expensive and difficult procedure. If it could be shown that the estimates of morbidity made by a single health agency approximated that estimate made using the total agency material, a significant short cut could be realized.

The materials discussed here concern the reliability of the reports concerning morbidity. For the first estimate of their reliability, teachers' estimates are compared with the total enumeration of morbidity as reported by all agencies. The second estimate concerns the teacher-supplied reports in the special survey and the reports maintained by the school system itself. A third estimate concerns a test-retest estimate of reliability: the data generated in the survey of

1961-1962 are compared to data collected on this same population in 1959. No attempt is made here to consider the validity of these reports.

The decision to carry out the school survey as a repeat of a survey done three years earlier was made because this provided an opportunity to measure the consistency of results between two surveys carried out in the same school system by essentially identical procedures. Although three years had brought a turnover of at least fifty per cent in the school population, morbidity rates of chronic conditions must be considered essentially as constants, so differences between the two surveys would, for the most part, be related to the unreliability or inconsistency of teachers as informants.

There was one significant disadvantage involved in the decision. For consistency the same check list was used as in the earlier study, and this did not include by name five of the thirteen conditions which the study was investigating. Although an "other" category gave an opportunity to list these, it was evident from the results that failure to mention these conditions specifically meant that they were largely unreported. This fact limits the meaningful comparison between the teachers' reports and the reports of all agencies to the eight conditions which were specifically listed.

Presented in Table 9 are the school teachers' estimates of the prevalence of handicapping conditions in the school population of the county and the total rates per thousand of these conditions as reported by all reporting agencies, including the school teachers' reports. All the medical and paramedical agencies of the county reported 4,083 handicapped children while the schools alone reported 902 children in the special survey. This represents about 22 per cent of the total number reported as handicapped in a school system enrolling about fifty-nine per cent of the population under twenty-one years of age.

Considering diagnoses rather than children, the school teachers report 1,259 medically significant conditions or 1.4 presumptive handicaps per child.

The teachers report 4.2 per cent *of the school population* as handicapped while the total agency report would indicate that approximately 11 per cent of the population under twenty-one years of age in Alamance County is handicapped.

The conclusion may be drawn from these data that school teachers significantly underestimate the prevalence of handicapped children. By comparison with estimates from the data of all agencies, for only one of the specifically listed conditions—speech defects—did

TABLE 9

The Prevalence Rates Per 1,000 Persons Under 21 of Various Handicapping Conditions as Reported by all Medical Agencies of Alamance County and the Schools of Alamance County, 1962. School Estimates are Based on School Population Only.

Condition	All Agency Rate	School Reported Rate
Orthopedic conditions	16	7
Epilepsy	2	1
Vision defects	14	2
Hearing defects	3	1
Cleft palate	1	1
Emotional disturbance	20	7
Speech disorders	16	17
Mental retardation:	28	21
Presumptive	(14)	(6)
Educable	(12)	(13)
Trainable	(1)	(2)
Custodial	(1)	....
Respiratory disorders	8	.3*
Heart conditions	5	.1*
Orthodontic conditions	2	....*
Cerebral palsy	2	.3*
Skin condition	2	....*
All other conditions	17	1.1*

* The symptom check list used in the survey of school teachers, a copy of which is in the Appendix, did not specify these conditions. The teachers were, however, free to list any other condition which they felt was medically significant.

teachers come up with a higher prevalence rate. Mental retardation was relatively well recognized. The most seriously underestimated condition was visual defects, a rather surprising finding, the reasons for which are not immediately clear.

The school system of the City of Burlington maintains a "Yearly Reporting Form" which is a method of reporting medical conditions to the school superintendent's office. By examining these "Yearly Reporting Forms," it is possible to compare the data generated by the special survey of school teachers with the records of conditions maintained by the school system itself. The reports with which the special survey data are compared were dated June, 1961, while the special survey was completed in February, 1962, and some differences may be attributable to change in the population. These data are presented in Table 10.

It is noteworthy that a greater number of conditions was reported in the school files than in the special survey. Part of this is certainly procedural: each school teacher was required to submit a report on every child in the yearly report, while instructions to the teachers concerning the special survey were to report only children who are handicapped.

TABLE 10

Comparison of the Numbers of Children Reported in the Special Survey and the Information Contained in a Standard Reporting Form on Health Used in the Burlington City Schools. Survey of February, 1962; Yearly Report Form of June, 1961.

Condition	Number of Reports Yearly School Form	Number of Reports Special Survey
Orthopedic conditions	16	70
Epilepsy	2	9
Vision defects	45	17
Hearing defects	28	17
Cleft palate	....	7
Emotional disturbance	58	64
Speech disorders	98	118
Mental retardation:	89	105
Presumptive	(18)	(33)
Educable	(50)	(101)
Trainable	(15)	(31)
Custodial	(6)	....
Respiratory disorders	93	4*
Heart conditions	20	....*
Orthodontic conditions	4	....*
Cerebral palsy	1	2*
Skin conditions	1	....*
Number of children	497	331

* The symptom check list used in this survey did not specify conditions of these types; the teachers were, however, free to list any other conditions which they felt were medically significant.

There are wide variations in the numbers reported for each condition, and this is especially true regarding those conditions which were not symptomatically described on the special survey form which was used. Chronic respiratory conditions, for example, were reported twenty-three times as frequently in the school reports as on the special survey. This is most probably due to the phenomenon of getting only what is asked for: these teachers, as concerned as they might be with such conditions as frequent colds or asthma, do not report these conditions on forms which do not specify "colds and asthma."

The best agreements between the numbers reported concern emotional disturbance, mental retardation and speech defects. Many more orthopedic conditions were reported in the special survey than on the school records. The same was true of epilepsy and cleft palate, though here the numbers are small.

These data in Table 10 would appear to indicate that school teachers must be asked about specific conditions. The use of residual "other" categories does not help at all. The areas of interest of school teachers: mental retardation, speech problems and emotional disorders appear to have the greatest stability under different reporting techniques. Improvement in special reporting forms will improve reliability, especially in areas in which the teachers may not be expected to show a great deal of interest. Finally, survey forms should be filled out by every teacher for every student as this would force each teacher to think through the health condition of each child. Unfortunately, these procedures place an additional burden on the teachers, and they must expect that the data so generated will be of use and will be used by the collecting agency.

The third estimate of teachers' reliability concerns the replication of the special survey itself. In the academic year 1958-1959, Doctor Ray B. Sizemore, under the auspices of the United Cerebral Palsy of North Carolina, completed a statewide school survey which used a form which was used again in the survey of 1961-1962. The data concerning Alamance County for the two surveys are presented in Table 11. These data suggest that there is a great deal of consistency of reporting by teachers.

TABLE 11

The Rates Per Thousand of Various Handicapping Conditions Reported by the School Teachers in Two Identical Special Surveys in Alamance County in the School Years of 1958-59 and 1961-62.

Condition	Survey of 1958-59	Survey of 1961-62
Orthopedic conditions	8	7
Epilepsy	1	1
Vision defects	2	2
Hearing defects	2	1
Cleft palate	1	1
Emotional disturbance	7	7
Speech disorders	14	17
Mental retardation:	18	21
Presumptive	(8)	(6)
Educable	(8)	(13)
Trainable	(2)	(2)
Respiratory disorders	....	....*
Heart conditions	....	....*
Orthodontic conditions	....	....*
Cerebral palsy	....	....*
Skin conditions	....	....*
Other	3	1
Number of children	841	902
School population	20,360	21,488
Percentage handicapped	4	4

* Condition not specified of the teachers in the check list. The teachers were, however, free to include this condition in the residual "Other" category.

In 1959 there were 841 presumptively handicapped children reported by teachers of Alamance County, and in 1962 there were 902 children reported. During this interval, school enrollment increased 5 per cent and this difference in reported children may be attributed to growth of the school system.

The most notable change in the reports appears to be in the categories of apparent retardation and in the classification of "educable retardation." This suggests, as the school superintendents have insisted, that the facilities for diagnosis and special education of the mentally retarded have increased. Similarly, an increase in the number of speech conditions during this period may be attributed to an increased awareness of speech problems. Essentially, the conclusion is that there appears to be a great deal of consistency in the reports elicited in surveys of this type.

There are some further questions which these data can answer: which children tend to remain in the school system as handicapped children and which tend to be removed from the system? For example, the 453 cases of mentally retarded children of the 1962 survey include 243 children similarly reported in 1959. This is slightly less than the expected changeover in school population by grades. Other conditions display less consistency: 80 per cent of the hearing conditions were new, 60 per cent of the epileptics reported were new, 30 per cent of the orthopedic conditions were new.

Presented in Table 12 is an interesting analysis of the reporting patterns revealed in the 1962 special school survey.

TABLE 12

The Number of School Children Reported and the
Reporting Rate per 100 Pupils by Grade

Grade in School	Number of Reports	Reporting Rate
1	100	5
2	113	6
3	95	6
4	87	4
5	62	4
6	62	4
7	62	2
8	33	2
9	36	2
10	23	2
11	1	....
12	6	1
Special Education	107	100
Grade Not Recorded	115	
TOTAL	902	

The numbers of children reported decrease with grade in school in a most striking fashion. The early grades present the greatest proportion of children reported, while the number of children reported by high school teachers is quite small. This decrease with advancing grade cannot be explained solely in terms of population changes. Two factors which may explain a portion of the observed differences are that handicapped children, as they proceed through the school system, make their ways into special education classes or into classes for the physically handicapped child, and that the drop-out rate for handicapped children is probably higher as they reach the high school level. In addition to these factors, the high school teacher does not have the acquaintance with his students which characterizes the grammar school teacher. Whatever factors and combinations are involved, it is clear that high school teachers do not report handicapped children with the frequency with which the grammar school teachers do.

Information was secured from the Department of Vocational Rehabilitation concerning a review of Alamance County's high school seniors which had been completed in May, 1962. The reports to that department, which were all self-referrals by the high school seniors, indicated that 100 high school seniors admitted some 112 medically significant conditions. These figures are to be contrasted with the six reports made by high school teachers of seniors.

Discussion

It was suggested at the beginning of this chapter that estimates of the prevalence rates of handicapping conditions in a community could be greatly simplified if it could be shown that estimates from a single agency approximated those from all agencies. It was hoped that the schools might be such a single agency. The results of these analyses lend little encouragement to this hope. School teachers proved to be rather consistent in the two special surveys, but, even for the conditions specifically listed, their reports seriously under-estimate all except one by comparison with the all-agency rates.

It is obvious that teachers cannot report on children not in school: those under six, over eighteen, dropouts and others who for any reason, including a handicapping condition, are not in school. Projections to the under six and eighteen to twenty-one groups and adjustments for those between those ages who are not in school might give a rough correction for these factors, provided the reports given by the teachers were reasonably accurate and complete for the school population.

There are several measures which might improve the adequacy of teachers' reporting. Listing all conditions on which reports are desired and requiring a report on each child would cut down sharply on the omission of conditions known to the teachers. The survey should be done late enough in the school year for the teachers to have become familiar with their pupils. If the schools maintain cumulative records including health data, these should be used in compiling the reports.

The fact that high school teachers have less knowledge of their individual pupils' problems requires that special consideration be given to the best ways to get information on high school children. The cumulative records, if available should be of help, and self-reporting by the children themselves is a possibility which might be more effective than reports prepared by the teachers.

Thus, while the contribution of teachers' reports in this study were disappointing, there were shortcomings in the procedures which were followed which can be corrected to produce a much more satisfactory result. It is important to note that the reliability of the school teachers' estimates is not at variance with the pattern for other agencies. Teachers report as large a segment of the population as is reported by the Welfare Department or the Health Department and shares with them the bias of special areas of interest and concern. It is probable that data secured through school teachers, incorporating these suggestions for improved reporting, would provide a better estimate than could be secured from any other single agency. Even so, an adequate picture of the prevalence of recognized handicapping problems in a community can be secured only by combining information from school teachers with that from all reporting sources.

CHAPTER IV

THE USEFULNESS OF HEALTH RECORDS

How useful are health records in estimating total prevalence of morbidity? Implicit in this question are several other, more basic, questions: What is it that health records measure? Are the health records of all agencies dealing with health matters equally useful? How do the estimates compiled using health records compare with estimates generated by other techniques? Are there specific conditions which are reliably estimated using health records?

It would seem at the outset that health records are biased estimates of morbidity in a population: health records concern only that segment of a population which has sought some assistance. Information may further be expected to vary within health agencies on the basis of the quantity and quality of records kept. Agencies maintain files for at least three partially independent reasons: as rational explanation of procedure, as in hospitals; as simple aids to memory, as in a physician's office; and for auditing and accounting purposes. Further, in larger health agencies, either publicly supported or privately financed, routine procedures are generally established and rationality apparently enhances the completeness of files. In public agencies, for example, the demand for adequate accounting generates relatively inclusive records. Smaller health agencies maintain records which are not nearly as complete or descriptive as those of the larger agencies. Further, the records of public agencies show a bias by socio-economic position since poor people seek public aid more often than other people and hence are over-represented in the better maintained public health records.

An examination of all medical records dealing with the children of Alamance County was a goal of the study. Prevalence estimates generated by means of the records review were to be compared with estimates generated by means of a household survey and with estimates based on clinical examinations of subsamples of youngsters reported either in the records or in the household survey. This chapter describes the findings of these comparisons.

The records review phase of this study began in October, 1961, and continued through November, 1962. Records were examined in state and local offices for public and private agencies, both large and small. Typical procedures were: state agencies, such as the Health

Department, were contacted at their Raleigh headquarters and permission to examine records was secured at that office. Local representatives were contacted through the state office, then directly by the study staff. Private physicians and dentists were contacted through their local societies and then in person by the staff. The special survey of all school teachers conducted for obtaining information from the schools has been described in Chapter III. In culling information from all files, a standardized reporting form was used. In all offices the handicapped child was defined by the study as the child whose name was given in response to the question, "What handicapped children are serviced by you?"

Files of Public and Private Agencies

Bias may exist in medical records. A potential form of bias is the differential servicing of population segments by public and private health agents. The first analysis presented for the medical records data is a comparison of the handicapping conditions reported by "public" and "private" agencies. Defined in this report as public agencies are: state and local health departments, Alamance County Welfare Department, Hospital Board of Control, State Department of Correction and Training, the Cerebral Palsy Hospital and the Alamance County school systems. The private agencies referred to here include: all physicians and dentists in practice in the county, the hospital records of Alamance County Hospital, Alamance General Hospital and North Carolina Memorial Hospital at Chapel Hill.

Health information was secured on 2,794 children from the public agencies of Alamance County and the state. These constituted 68 per cent of the 4,083 children reported by all agents. Considering reported conditions rather than children, the public agencies reported 62 per cent of the total of 4,874 conditions reported by all agencies. The number of diagnoses mades per child was 1.1 for public agencies, 1.4 for private agencies with an average for all agencies of 1.2 per child.

Presented in Table 13 are the rates of handicapping conditions per thousand of population under 21 years of age for the public files and for the total of all records. These data indicate that the public files contain sufficient data to permit the estimation of certain, generally very severe, handicapping conditions. Known to public health agencies are the numbers of cleft palate cases, the trainable and custodial mentally retarded, and the cerebral palsy cases. These conditions are beyond the means of familial care, and

TABLE 13

Prevalence Rates for Various Handicapping Conditions
Per 1,000 Persons Under 21
Public Files and Total File

Condition	Public Only	Total	Proportion Public/Total
Orthopedic conditions	11	16	.69
Epilepsy	1	2	.50
Vision defects	10	14	.71
Hearing defects	2	3	.67
Cleft palate	1	1	1.00
Emotional disturbance	14	20	.70
Speech disorders	13	16	.81
Mental retardation:	22	28	.79
Presumptive	(10)	(14)	
Educable	(10)	(12)	
Trainable	(1)	(1)	
Custodial	(1)	(1)	
Respiratory disorders	4	8	.50
Heart conditions	3	5	.60
Orthodontic conditions	....	2	....
Cerebral palsy	2	2	1.00
Skin conditions	1	2	.50
Other	14	17	.82

public agencies of the county know of the victims. This conclusion relates only to estimating the prevalence of conditions and not to individual case finding techniques.

For all other conditions the records of public agencies give a less adequate picture of the total number of cases known to both private and public agents. At least two factors probably act to reduce the proportion of cases in the public files: the ability of many families to provide care for less severe conditions and the limited availability of public care facilities. On the other hand, there are special community programs which place emphasis on certain conditions and result in increasing the proportion of total cases in public files. Examples are orthopedic conditions, vision defects and speech defects.

The proportion of the total number of reported handicapping conditions which can be expected to be found in the records of public agencies, then, appears to depend on three factors: the severity of the conditions, the availability and emphasis of public programs and facilities and the proportion of the population in the economic classes which look to public agencies for assistance in meeting medical needs. Since at least the last two factors vary from one community to another, it is clear that except for the severe conditions mentioned, cleft palate, trainable and custodial mentally retarded and cerebral palsy cases, the records of public agencies cannot be used to estimate the total number of conditions recorded in all health records.

Approximately two-thirds of the children reported as handicapped are reported in the public files. On this basis it would be a straightforward matter to estimate the number of children and, for that matter, conditions, as reported by all agencies. There is no way of knowing, however, that in all counties this same proportion would be known to the public agencies. It would be interesting to know if this proportion were consistent because the examination of public records is much simpler and faster than the examination of all health records. In Alamance such a simple adjustment as increasing the public rates by one-third estimates fairly accurately the rates from the total of all health records for the following conditions: orthopedic, vision, hearing, emotional disturbance, milder forms of mental retardation and skin conditions. Such a procedure overestimates the prevalence rates for cleft palate, severe mental retardation and cerebral palsy. Serious underestimates of prevalence based on medical records would be found for epilepsy and orthodontic conditions.

Having suggested that "severity" determines the search for public aid, and, therefore, inclusion in public records, one must speculate about the exception of epilepsy, certainly a serious condition. Epilepsy is one of those maladies which promotes secretiveness on the part of patients: it is still regarded as a social stigma. This probably prompts parents to seek private assistance for the condition. Further, since the condition can be controlled by the use of drugs, it is probably a clear option for parents, except the severely socio-economically deprived, to seek either public or private care.

As previously noted, orthodontic abnormalities, unless quite severe, did not appear to be perceived by either the health agents or the public of Alamance County as handicapping.

A final consideration to be given to these data in Table 13 involves the comparative difficulty of surveying private agencies. The Alamance County experience indicates that contacting physicians in private practice is very costly, time consuming and depressing. Despite all efforts, some response could be evoked from only 40 of the 62 physicians in practice in Alamance County. Of these, three pediatricians in the county reported 281, or 56 per cent, of the 504 children reported by all dentists and physicians. Of 223 reports made by dentists and physicians other than pediatricians, 65 per cent had been reported by some other source of information. The return from physicians in private practice in the county with regard to prevalence estimates (not case finding) was hardly worth the effort.

Medical Records and the Clinical Verification of Diagnoses

The medical records of health agents do not lend themselves to precise validation by clinical examinations for at least three reasons. First, and most important, parental or social concern for the well-being of a child is a function of numerous factors other than the existence of conditions recognizable as clinically significant by the physician. Second, for many reasons—some of which will be discussed below—information in medical records, including diagnoses, reflects several dimensions of social responsibility besides medical care. Third, medical conditions are often diagnosable only at times of acute stages of illness rather than at times which are convenient in conducting a health survey.

This section, which reports the results of a clinical examination of subsamples of children reported to be handicapped in medical records should not, therefore, be interpreted as a study of validity. It is not a study of the diagnostic acumen of health agents or agencies of Alamance County. Rather, it is in essence an analysis of the extent to which handicapping conditions in children are underestimated when the medical records of public agencies are examined *as if* they represented the totality of these problems which exist in the county.

The program of clinical examinations is described in some detail in Chapters II and VIII. It is sufficient here simply to point out that a sample of children drawn from two sources, the records of public agencies serving the county and children reported in a household survey of five per cent of the homes of the county as having or not having one of the specified handicapping conditions, were given comprehensive medical examinations including medical and social history, psychological tests, pediatric examination and all the special tests which were deemed appropriate in each case. Of the 456 children examined, 208 were known to public agencies. Those from agency files were selected randomly from lists of children classified by primary diagnosis, but no stratification of the sample in terms of age, sex, race or health agency was attempted.

The overall sampling rate was quite small, with 208 children of the reported 2,794 being examined, a rate of 7 per cent. The rates for individual diagnostic categories varied from 50 per cent of the cleft palate cases to 4 per cent of those emotionally disturbed. As noted in Chapter II the three factors which influenced the rates of invitation were: the number of children reported to have a particular condition, the requirements of the clinic itself, and the minimum number required to provide some reliable estimate of the prevalence of the condition being examined. Of course, the data presented here are based only on the children examined at the clinic. Some who were invited did not, for one reason or another, attend. A further limitation is that sampling was based only on the records of public agencies; the decision to omit the records of private practitioners was made in the interest of preserving their confidentiality.

As far as reported conditions are concerned, it was possible to verify their existence in 95 per cent of the children examined, a remarkable measure of verification.

On the other hand, the extent to which handicapping conditions are underestimated when the records of public agencies are used as the basis of estimating prevalence rates is shown in Table 14. Comparison of columns (1) and (2) makes clear that the records of public agencies fail to include a large proportion of handicapping conditions which exist in children who are recorded as having some handicapping conditions. Only in the case of epilepsy did the clinical examinations fail to show a significantly higher number of conditions than were reported in the records. For nine of the 13 conditions the adjusted rates are more than twice as high as those based on the records only.

TABLE 14

Prevalence Rates of Handicapping Conditions Per 1,000 Persons Under 21 as Estimated From the Public Files of the County and Clinically Adjusted Rates of Children From Public Files and the Household Survey.

	Public Files		Adjusted Estimates
Condition	Unadjusted	Adjusted	Household Survey*
Orthopedic conditions	11	16	13
Epilepsy	1	1	12
Vision defects	10	37	27
Hearing defects	2	14	9
Cleft palate	1	2	2
Emotional disturbance	14	34	52
Speech disorders	13	30	12
Mental retardation:	22	26	77
Presumptive	(10)	(3)	
Educable	(10)	(21)	
Trainable	(1)	(1)	
Custodial	(1)	(1)	
Respiratory disorders	4	8	29
Heart conditions	3	16	4
Orthodontic conditions	1	6	37
Cerebral palsy	2	9	6
Skin conditions	1	4	11

* Moderate and severe only.

In addition to the assumption, obviously wide of the mark, that the files of the public agencies record all the known handicapped children in the county, these data involve two other assumptions thought to be valid: first, that the children who attended the clinic were representative of all who were invited, and, second, that the selection of children was on the basis of a random sample of the children known to all health agencies of the county. In other words, the random assignment of children to diagnostic categories on the basis of a primary diagnosis made by a primary agent does not bias the overall prevalence estimates made here.

The adjustment procedure employed in the second column of Table 14 may be described as follows: each child examined in the clinic "represented" a certain segment of the "handicapped child population." In the case of the cleft palate sample, for example, each child represented two children since the sampling ratio was one-half. For all other conditions, the inverse of the sampling ratio served as a "weighting factor" in restructuring the handicapped child population. Thus, the "adjusted prevalence estimates" are estimates of the total prevalence of handicapping conditions in Alamance County based on the results of examinations of the sample of children with medical records.

We believe the best estimates of the prevalence rates of handicapping conditions in Alamance County are those derived from the clinical examination of a sample of children reported in the household survey. This sample included children reported both as presumptively handicapped and as presumptively normal. These rates are shown in the last column of Table 5, Chapter II, based on children whose conditions resulted in moderate or severe disability.

With the exception of speech defects these adjusted survey rates are all higher than those derived from the public records. For three other categories, orthopedic conditions, cleft palate and heart conditions, the difference was not great. However, even these differences assume greater significance in the light of the fact that in the adjusted survey figures children whose conditions caused minimal or no disability have been excluded. It was not possible to classify agency reported cases by the degree of disability, but, in the clinical examinations of the sample of children drawn from this source, many of the reported conditions were not found to cause significant disability.

For the other nine conditions, epilepsy, visual and hearing defects, emotional disturbance, mental retardation, chronic respiratory disease, orthodontic conditions, cerebral palsy and skin conditions, the adjusted survey rates were more than twice as high as the agency record rates. Thus, rates derived from the medical records of health agencies not only seriously underestimated the prevalence of handi-capping conditions, but the degree of the underestimation for the several specific conditions varied widely. It is obvious, therefore, that these records do not provide a usable basis for estimating the prevalence of handicapping conditions.

Comment

Why should existing medical records provide such an inadequate picture of childhood handicapping conditions? There are, of course, many factors involved. Some relate to the records of both private practitioners and public agencies, and some are unique to the records of public agencies. Since some of these factors account for a part of the gaps and inadequacies of services for meeting the needs of handicapped children, they deserve comment.

It is obvious, first of all, that medical files contain records only of individuals for whom some service has been sought plus those who have been reported as a result of special case finding efforts, such as the screening program for school children. Those conditions which have not been recognized or for which, although recognized, no service has been sought are not included.

A second factor is the specialized character of much of medical service today, a result of the growth of specialization in medical practice and the specialized character of many public facilities and programs for the handicapped. The child for whom attention is sought for a particular condition may receive the care required by that condition, without recognition of other coexisting conditions. In Alamance County, as in many other communities, there are available, through private practitioners and public facilities, a wide range of specialized services, but, except for the minority of children who receive continuing well-child supervision from pediatricians or family physicians, there is no provision for the child to be viewed as a whole, or for attention to be given to the total range of his problems and their interrelationships.

Another factor is that of definition. Many of the diagnoses in physician and agency records were based on inclusive definitions. For example, a diagnosis of cleft palate subsumes orthodontic defect and speech defect. Such inclusive diagnoses seemed to be the rule in Alamance County.

In addition to these factors which apply to both physician and agency records, there are others which relate only to agency records. Conditions for which there are special publicly supported programs or facilities are disproportionately represented, especially where admission or referral must be made through a public agency. Restrictions on public agencies either by law or agency policy are important in excluding certain of the handicapped from their services. Financial eligibility is required for many services which are received through Welfare Department referral. Programs and facilities for specific categories of handicaps have specific eligibility requirements which eliminate some children. An example would be the interest some school teachers have in speech defects.

Aside from legal or policy requirements, agencies tend to have special interests and emphases which are derived from special community interest or support or from the interests of individual workers and which result in certain conditions receiving much more attention than others.

The fact that records are relatively complete for those severe conditions which need care transcending the ability of the average family to provide has been referred to earlier.

For the purpose of the present report these factors are of primary interest as explanations of the inadequacies of medical records as a basis for estimating prevalence rates. Beyond this, however, they reveal highly significant gaps and inadequacies in meeting the needs of handicapped children. These gaps and inadequacies are discussed and possible steps toward some solutions are suggested in Chapter X.

Summary

Medical records do not provide a satisfactory basis for estimating the prevalence of handicapping conditions in children. They seriously underestimate prevalence as estimated by other means, and the degree of underestimation varies greatly for different conditions. Many factors are involved, including specialization of practitioners and agencies, legal and policy limitations on agency services, lack of coordination, the use of inclusive definitions, and the fact that medical records include primarily those who have sought service.

Some of these factors reveal serious gaps and inadequacies in meeting the needs of handicapped children which call for careful study and efforts to develop needed solutions.

CHAPTER V

INTERAGENCY REFERRAL PATTERNS

An opportunity to study patterns of interagency referrals was provided since the information on interagency referrals was systematically recorded on the schedule concerning handicapped children known to the health agencies of the county. These health agencies included hospitals, physicians, schools, clinics, and special hospitals throughout the state of North Carolina. Information concerning the referral, or *who is sent where by whom,* was recorded on a standard schedule* from 5,953 medical records concerning 4,083 children reported to be physically, mentally, or emotionally handicapped. It is with these data that two general exploratory questions were investigated: (1) what interagency referral ties really exist as reported in agency files, and (2) what socio-personal characteristics relate to the referral process.

Organizational Goals, Societal Ethics, and Interagency Referrals

Stated briefly, the goal of social service is the prevention of dependency. Where this goal is not met, there emerges a secondary goal of rehabilitation. Goals by definition are unmet since, once achieved, they are incapable of motivating further accomplishment. The goals of prevention and rehabilitation, then, serve to direct and focus the activities of an agency. For an agency to survive in society its goals must be held as legitimate, or valued by the society. Not only the ends which the organization seeks to accomplish, but also the means to these ends must be held as legitimate. That is, they cannot go against the dominant values of the society. In democratic societies this legitimation of means is not easy; incongruous and conflicting values and ethics exist simultaneously.

Two conflicting ethics guide agencies dedicated to the goals of social service. Both serve to create, yet also to limit the operations of agencies. One ethic stresses social awareness and public responsibility while the other stresses individual responsibility. The former allows the formation of public and private agencies and legitimates their operations; the latter prevents the agency from forcing its services upon the client. Thus both referral and the follow-up of referral

---

* See Appendix.

are directly implicated in the behavioral manifestations of these conflicting, yet simultaneously existing, ethics.

Referrals represent a process which is of special concern in an age in which medical specialization creates the necessity of coordination, cooperation, and division of labor among health facilities. It has been suggested that a lack of coordination between already existing health services may be a major cause for the failure in efforts to treat the "whole child." One index of coordination of effort is the referral of children between health agencies. Thus the examination of patterns of referral existing between the social agencies of a county is of both theoretical and practical concern.

A Model of Complex Organization

One method of describing the behavior of medical agencies is to construct a model or "ideal-type" of referral system with which the functioning of real agencies may be contrasted. This approach allows the interjection of theory in the form of the goals of the organization and the ethics of the society. In short, it allows some theoretical meat for the skeleton of empiricism.

The model of interagency referral used in this paper is based upon assumptions drawn from the ethics of a truly charitable and socially concerned society. They are: (1) all agencies have as their goal helping the child; (2) if a particular agency cannot meet the particular needs of a child, it will make the necessary referral to an agency where aid can be received; (3) if needs beyond those for which aid was requested are recognized, the additional needs will be met; (4) the personal characteristics of the child should make no difference in the quality of aid he receives; (5) no medical agency is capable, medically, financially, or legally of caring for the "whole child."

In summary, the model states that the giving of a referral by a health agency should depend upon the medically relevant conditions affecting the child who has come for assistance and the services available at the health agency to which the child has appealed. It is known, however, that agencies do not in practice make referrals on such a straightforward and uncomplicated basis. Organizational factors such as the need to further public support or interpersonal rivalries among personnel, and social facts such as discriminatory practices based upon the socio-economic characteristics of the client affect the operation of agencies.

Limitations of the Data

Before proceeding, it is necessary to mention some of the limitations of the data. Not all the health agencies' files could be examined. The files at Duke Medical Center in Durham, the largest general hospital and center for medical specialists, were maintained in such a fashion as to make their inclusion impractical and are, unfortunately, omitted. Then, too, it is possible that not all the referrals were written into the medical records which were examined. Private physicians may, for example, send a child to a specialist and never record this information. Furthermore, it is unusual to find a record of a formal referral in health files which had no provision for such reports. Also, records are listed in terms of the "primary diagnosis," or the principal handicap affecting the child. When several conditions affect the child, it is sometimes unclear what the *principal* handicap is. Indeed, it is often difficult to establish *if* the child is really handicapped, and if he is, whether the physical condition or his psychological adjustment to it is really the handicap. Then there is the generality of our use of the term "health agency." In essence a health agency is a source of information concerning health needs and practices. Under this definition schools, physicians, the State Board of Health, and private charities, are all health agencies. Finally, the reports of school teachers deserve special notice. The schools do not list any referrals because the data reported from the two school systems of the county were based upon school teachers' reports which did not elicit information concerning referrals.

The Interagency Sociogram

The discussion up to this point has been designed to provide an introduction to what we shall term an interagency sociogram. Specifically, the sociogram is a map of the interagency relationships which exist as a result of the referrals which agencies give to their clients. In the aggregate, these data provide a picture of one aspect of medical care for handicapped children in Alamance County.

The social and medical agencies of Alamance County by frequency and rate of referral are presented in Table 15. Twenty-two agencies made referrals to 33 other agencies, thus suggesting a core of referring agencies directing children to specialized and non-referring agencies. Referrals were given to twenty-seven different agencies by the Welfare Department, more than were given by any other agency. The Health Department was next in the variety of agencies to which its clients were referred, followed by physicians in private practice and the State Board of Health. Hospitals and institutional homes gave relatively few referrals since presumably they are capable of handling a great variety of their own problems. Charities servicing the county do not record any referrals.

TABLE 15

Agencies by Rates of Referrals Given

Source Agency	Total No. of Reports	% Referral of Total Reports	Agencies to Which Referrals are Made
Welfare Department	923	30	27
Health Department, orthopedic	310	45	10
Health Department, psychiatric	163	7	6
Health Department, P.H. nurse	526	65	21
C.C.S. State Board of Health[1]	297	20	10
Epidem. State Board of Health	69	0	....
Vocational Rehabilitation	100	1	1
State Commission for Blind	38	50	9
Murdoch School	59	68	2
O'Berry School	14	50	1
Dix Hill Hospital	3	33	1
Mental Health St. Bd. Health	199	0	....
Schools for Blind, Deaf	17	0	....
N. C. Cerebral Palsy Hospital	68	6	3
Burlington schools	331	0	....
Alamance schools	571	0	....
Nurseries	20	0	....
City school yearly sheet	497	4	1
Sizemore study (schools) *	464	0	....
N.C.M.H. pediatrics[2]	58	3	2
N.C.M.H. psychiatric	210	0	....
Alamance County Hospital	462	12	7
Alamance General Hospital	27	15	3
Dr. A.)	92	61	11
Dr. B.)	43	33	5
Dr. C.) Pediatricians	24	54	3
Dr. D.)	2	100	1
General practitioners	76	50	11
Internists	32	38	5
Other physicians	50	24	5
Dentists	76	16	4
United Cerebral Palsy	55	0	....
Nat. Soc. for Crippled Children	14	0	....
Nat. Soc. for Retarded Children	64	0	....
Total	5,593		

* Special canvass of schools done in 1959 by Dr. Ray B. Sizemore.
1. Crippled Children's Section.
2. North Carolina Memorial Hospital.

The agencies which received referrals tabulated by the number of agencies making these referrals is presented in Table 16. A noticeable contrast is that the Welfare Department ranks low on referrals received, whereas it ranked high on referrals given. It is also noticed that the Crippled Children's Section of the State Board of Health is the largest recipient of referrals. This agency performs the services of providing hospital referrals and prosthetic devices to needy children. Duke Hospital in Durham, the largest medical center in the area, was the second largest receiver of referrals and ranked with North Carolina Memorial Hospital at Chapel Hill in the number of different agencies making referrals to it. Private physicians and institutional schools received referrals from several agencies. Specialized facilities, such as the Cerebral Palsy Hospital in Durham, also received a fair number of referrals from a few agencies. In summary, however, the important contrast seems to be between agencies which normally *give* referrals and those which normally *receive* referrals.

TABLE 16

Agencies Receiving Referrals

Referral Agency	Number of Referrals Received	Number of Agencies Making These Referrals
Welfare Department	12	7
Health Department, orthopedic	0	0
Health Department, psychiatric	8	3
Health Department, P.H. nurse	3	2
C.C.S. State Board of Health[1]	196	6
State Board of Correction	3	1
Vocational Rehabilitation	3	3
State Commission for Blind	11	2
Murdoch Hospital	94	8
Cherry Hospital	1	1
O'Berry School	19	4
John Umstead Hospital	3	2
Caswell School	19	4
Mental Health, St. Bd. Health	2	2
Schools for Blind, Deaf	16	6
N. C. Cerebral Palsy Hospital	25	5
N. C. Orthopedic Hospital	11	3
Burlington schools	20	3
Alamance schools	37	3
Private schools	1	1
Juvenile courts	9	1
N.C.M.H. pediatrics[2]	145	15
N.C.M.H. psychiatric	39	8
Duke Hospital	176	15
Alamance County Hospital	3	3
Other hospitals	22	10
N. C. Convalescent Hospital	2	2
McPherson Hospital	2	2
Dr. A.)	3	3
Dr. B.) Pediatricians	3	2
General practitioners	2	1
Internists	1	1
Other physicians	154	9
Dentists	6	1

1. Crippled Children's Section.
2. North Carolina Memorial Hospital.

The agencies to which referrals were given and from which referrals were received are determined by a cross-classification table which is not presented in this report. From it the following relationships are determined: the Welfare Department, which gives referrals to the largest variety of health agencies, gives most of its referrals to the Crippled Children's Section of the State Board of Health where money may be obtained for medical treatment. Murdoch School for retardates also stands high on the list of agencies to which the Welfare Department refers its clients; this is understandable in that the Welfare Department is the legally constituted source of admission to the state centers for the retarded. Interagency relationships exist between the Welfare Department and the Psychiatric Section of North Carolina Memorial Hospital, as well as the special state schools in addition to Murdoch. There are ties, too, to the public school systems of the county regarding the schools' special education program for retarded children. The Office of Vocational Rehabilitation, the State Commission for the Blind, and Cherry and John Umstead Hospitals, two state hospitals for the mentally retarded, were also utilized as potential assistance providers by the Welfare Department. A few cases were referred by the Welfare Department to the state schools for the blind and deaf and to the Cerebral Palsy Hospital.

In summary, the Welfare Department seems to have its closest ties with state and county agencies such as homes for mental retardates and other state-supported institutions. Referrals are also given to medical specialists. Little formal appeal is made to private charities. The Welfare Department, then, may be viewed, in the light of the referrals which it makes, as serving a function of recognition and introduction to specialized state agencies.

The next agency, in terms of the variety of referral agencies, is the Department of Health. The majority of its referrals are to physicians in private practice in the county. Referrals are also sent to specialty hospitals like the North Carolina Convalescent Hospital and McPherson Hospital as well as to the Crippled Children's Section of the State Board of Health. North Carolina Memorial Hospital and Duke Hospital are given numerous referrals, whereas the two local county hospitals are given none. It is noteworthy that the two agencies discussed so far have little formal interchange of clients. The Welfare Department gave only five referrals to the Health Department and the Health Department only five referrals to the Welfare Department. The only private charity mentioned by the Health Department was the Lion's Club and, indeed, outside of the Welfare and Health Department, no other agency records making a referral to a private charity.

We have described the two largest agencies in terms of their referral-giving and referral-receiving relationships with other agencies in the county and surrounding counties. These data lead us to conclude that the two agencies do not exchange clients with one another to any significant extent. Furthermore, they seem to have different "channels of communication" in the community.

Factors Related to the Giving of Referrals

The next analysis of the factors related to referral is limited to the Welfare and Health Departments and is presented in terms of a multiple regression analysis. Both the dependent and independent variables are categoric or binary variates.[1] While the data do not in the strictest sense meet the assumptions of linear regression, Warner has argued that when the sample gets large, the binary vectors under regression approach normality.[2] Rigorous induction is not the primary purpose here. The regression equations and tests of hypotheses below are presented in a descriptive sense to summarize a large amount of material and to try to isolate causal variables in the system of variables presented.

According to the theoretical model developed earlier, referral *should be unrelated* to sex, race and the person responsible for making the diagnosis but *should be related* to the primary diagnosis (presumed handicapping condition), the agency's involvement with the case, and whether or not the child had more than one handicapping condition. That is, referral should be based upon the medical conditions affecting the child and the provisions of the agency for care or treatment.

A comparison between the regression equations for the entire predictor set for the Welfare and Health Departments is presented in Table 17. For both departments, the predictor set enables statistical prediction of whether or not referral was given. The analysis of variance for the Welfare Department gives a variance ratio of 3.95 with 22 and 900 degrees of freedom. This is statistically significant at the .001 level. For the Health Department the variance ratio is

---

1. For a description of this technique see: Joe H. Ward, Jr., "Multiple Regression Models," in Harold Borko (ed.), *Computer Applications in the Behavioral Sciences*. (Englewood Cliffs: Prentice-Hall, 1962), pp. 204-237.
2. Stanley L. Warner, "Multivariate Regression of Dummy Variates Under Normality Assumptions," *Journal of the American Statistical Association* 58 (December, 1963), pp. 1054-1063.

16.02 with 20 and 976 degrees of freedom, also significant at the .001 level.

TABLE 17

Prediction of Referral for the Welfare and Health Departments

Variable	Welfare	Health
Y Intercept	0.27	0.33
Sex	0.00	—0.02
Race	0.02	—0.12
Diagnostic categories:		
Orthopedic conditions	—0.38	0.12
Epilepsy	—0.21	0.10
Vision defects	—0.03	0.21
Hearing defects	0.30	0.66
Cleft palate	0.11	0.37
Emotional disturbance	—0.02	—0.01
Speech disorders	—0.31	—0.01
Mental retardation	—0.01	0.17
Respiratory disorders	—0.05	0.07
Heart conditions	—0.08	0.26
Orthodontic conditions	—0.46	*
Cerebral palsy	0.29	0.23
Skin conditions	—0.14	—0.23
Diagnostician:		
Social worker	0.00	*
Staff psychiatrist	0.18	—0.13
Nurse or physician	0.13	0.37
Agency involvement:		
Home supervision	—0.17	—0.11
Diagnostic study	—0.20	—0.18
Medical supervision	—0.03	—0.43
Multiple handicap	0.02	0.07

* No information available.

There are many interesting comparisons between the variables presented for the two systems.

Sex: this variable was not a significant factor for either agency.

Race: color was not a significant factor for the Welfare Department, but for the Health Department being Negro was negatively related to receiving a referral.

Diagnostic categories: orthopedic handicaps, epilepsy, and vision were negatively related to receiving a referral from the Welfare Department, whereas they were positively related for the Health Department. Hearing and cleft palate handicaps were positively related to referral for both agencies. Emotional handicaps had a low association with referral for both agencies. Speech handicaps were negatively associated with referral for the Welfare Department but had no association with referral for the Health Department. Mental retardation was not related to referral for the Welfare Department but was positively associated with referral for the Health Department. Respiratory problems were not highly related to referral for either department, but the trend was toward a negative association for the Welfare Department and a positive association for the Health Department. Heart problems were negatively associated with referral for the Welfare Department but positively related for the Health Department. Orthodontic defects were negatively associated with referral for the Welfare Department. Too few diagnoses of orthodontic defects were made by the Health Department to permit reliable estimates. Cerebral palsy was positively associated with referral for both agencies. Skin defects were negatively associated with referral for both agencies.

Diagnostician: social workers were neither positively nor negatively associated with referral for the Welfare Department. The Health Department, of course, does not hire social workers so there is no basis for comparison between the two agencies. For the Welfare Department, diagnosis by a staff psychiatrist was positively related to receiving a referral. Diagnosis by a nurse or physician was positively related to referral for both agencies only more strongly so for the Health Department.

Agency involvement: only medically related types of agency involvement were included in the regression equation. Both agencies have a wide variety of tasks they perform for their clients. It is interesting, therefore, but not surprising that all types of medical involvement were negatively associated with referral to other agencies. The most negative association was for medical supervision by the Health Department.

Multiple handicap: being multiply handicapped has only a slightly higher relationship to referral than being singly handicapped.

The total regression model for prediction is not a complete picture of the regression; it is necessary also to examine the redundancy of information among the independent variables. Any given variable may be a predictor in itself; it may, however, offer little, given the other information in the system, because of high intercorrelations among the variables. It is possible to examine this aspect of redundancy by computing the loss of prediction when the model is restricted by a given variable; that is, it is taken out of the system.

For the Welfare Department, when the medical diagnoses are removed from the system there is a significant loss in prediction indicating that the effect is "pure" rather than a spurious effect caused by high intercorrelation with other components within the system. The variance ratio for loss of prediction is 1.82 with 13 and 900 degrees of freedom which is significant at less than the .05 level.

The important factors, in addition to the medical diagnoses, were the diagnostician and the agency's involvement with the case. When each of these factors was removed one at a time from the system, there was a significant loss of prediction. For the category of diagnostician, the variance ratio was 7.92, which is significant at less than the .001 level with 3 and 900 degrees of freedom. When the category of agency involvement was removed, it produced a variance ratio of 10.45 with 3 and 900 degrees of freedom, statistically significant at less than the .001 level.

The conclusion drawn from these data is that for the Welfare Department, the factors involved in whether or not a child was given a referral were the medical diagnosis, the diagnostician or person working with the child, and the extent of the agency's involvement with the child. This finding places the Welfare Department in fairly close accord with the theoretical model, but does suggest that factors other than the medical, such as bias in terms of the diagnostician, are also involved.

A similar analysis completed for the Health Department data showed that the medical diagnoses, the diagnostician, and the involvement of the agency again predicted to referral. For the Health Department, the race of the client was also a factor; when race was removed from the system, there was a statistically significant loss of prediction: the variance ratio was 8.36 with 1 and 976 degrees of freedom which is significant at less than the .001 level. The category of diagnostician produced a variance ratio for loss of 48.51 with 2 and 976 degrees of freedom; agency involvement with the case produced a variance ratio of 22.67 with 3 and 976 degrees of freedom. Both ratios are significant at less than the .001 level.

In terms of the theoretical model described earlier, both the Health and Welfare Departments of Alamance County make referrals in terms other than those of simple medical disability: organizational and structural factors are also effective, such as the person by whom the child is seen. The data also show that, for the Health Department, there is bias in referral depending upon whether the patient is white or Negro. White children receive more referrals than Negro children. This finding deserves careful exploration. In terms of the theoretical model, the Health Department would present more of a contrast with the ideal-type than the Welfare Department.

Factors Relating To Type of Agency To Which Referral Is Made

In the previous section of this chapter it was established that within this universe of data there was some evidence to indicate that the Welfare Department was slightly biased in the giving of referrals. That is, the person responsible for making the diagnosis seemed to be important along with the medical factors. For the Health Department there was an additional slight bias, namely by race, in favor of giving referrals to white children. Careful examination of the data showed that this was a bias favoring referral by nurses and disfavoring referral by psychologists. These findings lead to two additional questions. First, what factors determine the general kind of agency to which the child is referred? Second, what factors are related to the follow-up of referral? It is at this level of analysis that the operation of the agencies can be seen as functioning in a community setting. Furthermore, the follow-up of a referral is not made by isolated individuals in a community devoid of social structure. The values of sub-groups within the society undoubtedly influence where a person goes to seek aid in the first place, and secondly, whether or not he will follow up a referral to any particular agency. It is here that we become less sure of the data we have. Files had to be matched by name with all the potential errors of dealing with children's names, nicknames and parental name changes through divorce and re-marriage. Furthermore, it should be remembered that follow-ups to Duke Hospital are not included, thus lowering the rate of follow-up of referral to private hospitals. For the subsequent analysis the two large departments are combined in order to focus on general trends rather than on two separate analyses.

A determination of the type of agency to which the patient is referred is accomplished by a comparison of the regression coefficients presented in Table 18. The following discussion presents some important findings and contrasts between the referrals which are sent to state agencies, schools and hospitals.

Sex: this factor did not differentially affect referrals to any of the kinds of agencies.

Race: Negroes were less likely than whites to be referred to state agencies or schools, but were more likely to be referred to hospitals.

Diagnostic categories: orthopedic handicaps and epilepsy were unlikely to be referred to state agencies and schools, but were likely to be referred to hospitals. Vision handicaps were likely to be referred to state agencies and unlikely to be referred to

TABLE 18

Prediction of Referral By Type of Agency to Which
Referral Is Made

| Variable | Type of Referral Agency | | |
	State	School	Hospital
Y Intercept	0.11	0.27	0.00
Sex	0.02	—0.01	—0.01
Race	—0.04	—0.03	0.08
Diagnostic categories:			
Orthopedic conditions	—0.02	—0.05	0.12
Epilepsy	—0.03	—0.08	0.49
Vision defects	0.04	—0.07	—0.14
Hearing defects	—0.08	—0.15	0.03
Cleft palate	—0.03	—0.03	0.27
Emotional disturbance	—0.05	0.03	0.28
Speech disorders	—0.04	0.12	0.00
Mental retardation	0.42	0.02	0.00
Respiratory disorders	—0.01	—0.05	0.71
Heart conditions	—0.03	—0.02	0.33
Orthodontic conditions	—0.06	—0.10	0.06
Cerebral palsy	0.24	—0.08	0.04
Skin conditions	—0.02	0.10	0.07
Diagnostician:			
Social worker	0.22	—0.14	0.14
Staff psychiatrist	0.27	—0.21	—0.02
Nurse or physician	—0.04	—0.16	0.09
Agency involvement:			
Home supervision	—0.02	0.11	0.00
Diagnostic study	—0.05	0.05	—0.02
Medical supervision	—0.02	—0.04	—0.08
Multiple handicap	—0.06	0.02	0.19

schools and hospitals. Hearing defects were unlikely to be referred to state agencies and schools, but were likely to be referred to hospitals. Emotional problems were unlikely to be referred to state agencies and have very little relationship with referral to schools; they were likely to be referred to hospitals. Speech problems were most likely to be referred to schools. Mental retardation was strongly associated with referral to state agencies. Respiratory problems, on the other hand, were highly associated with referrals to hospitals as were heart defects, and to a lesser extent, orthodontic defects. State agencies were the object of referral for cases of cerebral palsy. Skin defects were as likely to be referred to schools as hospitals.

Diagnostician: referral by a social worker was likely to be to a state agency or hospital, but unlikely to be to a school. When the referral was made by a staff psychiatrist it was likely to be to a state agency, and unlikely to be to a school. Nurses, on the other hand, were likely to make referrals only to hospitals.

Agency involvement: home supervision and diagnostic study were positively related only to referrals to schools. Medical supervision was not positively related to referrals for any of the classes of referral agencies.

Multiple handicap: a decided contrast exists for referrals made to multiply handicapped children: they were especially likely to be sent to private hospitals and especially unlikely to be sent to state agencies.

Factors Related To The Follow-up of Referrals

The final question which will be asked in this analysis is that of what factors relate to the client's following-up a referral to a new agency. A comparison of the regression equations for prediction of the follow-up of referral is made by class of referral agency. These data are presented in Table 19.

The data for follow-up of referral indicates the following results:

Sex: sex was not related to the follow-up of referral to different classes of agencies.

Race: differences by race are small but where a trend can be seen to exist it would favor the follow-up of referral to hospitals by Negroes and to favor the follow-up of referrals to state agencies by whites.

Diagnostic categories: orthopedic handicaps were not related to a differential follow-up of referral by class of agency. Epileptics were especially likely to follow up referrals to private hospitals but not to other kinds of agencies. Vision, hearing and cleft

TABLE 19

Prediction of Follow-Up of Referral By Type of Agency

Variable	Type of Referral Agency		
	State	School	Hospital
Y Intercept	0.04	0.01	0.05
Sex	0.00	0.00	0.01
Race	—0.03	0.01	0.02
Diagnostic categories:			
Orthopedic conditions	—0.01	0.02	—0.01
Epilepsy	—0.02	0.01	0.26
Vision defects	—0.02	—0.01	—0.02
Hearing defects	—0.02	—0.01	0.00
Cleft palate	—0.03	0.01	—0.02
Emotional disturbance	—0.06	0.01	0.17
Speech disorders	—0.02	0.17	—0.02
Mental retardation	0.18	0.06	0.02
Respiratory disorders	—0.01	0.01	0.09
Heart conditions	—0.03	0.01	—0.01
Orthodontic conditions	—0.03	0.00	—0.01
Cerebral palsy	0.18	0.02	0.02
Skin conditions	0.00	0.00	—0.03
Diagnostician:			
Social worker	0.04	—0.06	—0.05
Staff psychiatrist	0.19	—0.07	0.01
Nurse or physician	0.03	—0.03	0.04
Agency involvement:			
Home supervision	0.00	0.00	0.00
Diagnostic study	—0.02	0.04	0.00
Medical supervision	—0.03	—0.01	—0.04
Multiple handicap	—0.03	—0.01	0.02

palate handicaps were not related to the follow-up of referral to any great extent. Persons with emotional handicaps were especially likely to go to private hospitals and especially unlikely to go to state supported psychiatric facilities. Another way of saying this is that persons with emotional handicaps were most likely to be directed to psychiatric aid and least likely to be coerced into residential confinement. Persons with speech problems were likely to follow up referrals to schools where speech therapy is available. Mental retardation was most highly associated with follow-up of referrals to state supported facilities for the retarded and second most likely with seeking special education classes in the public schools. Persons with respiratory problems were most likely to follow up referrals to private hospitals. Neither heart diseases nor orthodontic defects were highly differentially related to follow-up of referral. Persons with cerebral palsy were very likely to follow up referrals to state hospitals. Skin defects were not related to follow-up of referrals, especially to hospitals.

Diagnostician: when a social worker made the diagnosis, the person was most likely to follow up a referral to a state hospital and least likely to follow up referrals to schools and hospitals. Diagnosis by a staff psychiatrist was strongly related to the follow-up of referrals to state agencies. When the diagnosis was made by a nurse, the person was most likely to follow up a referral which was made to a state or private hospital, but not to a public school.

Agency involvement: when the person was under home supervision he was neither likely nor unlikely to follow up a referral regardless of the class of agency. If a person were under diagnostic study, he was likely to follow up a referral to a public school but less likely to follow up a referral to a state agency. Medical supervision was negatively related to the follow-up of referrals, especially to private hospitals.

Multiple handicap: whether or not the patient had a multiple handicap does not seem to be related very strongly to the follow-up of referrals. The trend seems to be for multiply handicapped not to follow up referrals to state agencies but to follow up referrals to private hospitals.

Discussion

There are two different kinds of interpretation possible from these data. The first, and perhaps the most important, is judgmental. These data provide information concerning such questions as, "Is this the way things ought to be?" "Given the goals of health agencies and the community's resources, is this the best organization which can exist?" The second kind of question concerns a more typical product of research efforts, "What hypotheses for future research have been uncovered by this investigation?"

Given the limitations of the data used in this report, judgments should be made only with a great deal of caution. Insight into complex organization must be descriptive of the whole goal-directed processes and functioning of the organizations. In this chapter the focus has been limited to referral patterns only. The adequacy of treatment afforded to a particular child is not considered.

Still, some patterns do emerge rather clearly. The Health and Welfare Departments of Alamance County do not refer cases to one another. It is difficult to understand why more interagency activity of this sort does not exist, especially in terms of the large numbers of referrals made by these agencies. Furthermore, there is a strong implication of two distinct channels of aid and referral depending upon which major agency a child went to first.

It has also been found that the multiply handicapped child tends not to be given referrals to state health agencies. This may be a function of legally prescribed functions and areas of concern which are too restrictive to fit the patient's needs and conditions. This is an area of concern because seriously disabled children tend to be multiply handicapped. If adequate socially supported medical and psychological services are to be provided, agencies with a wider range of services or fewer legal restrictions are necessary.

Throughout this discussion the assumption has been made that referrals are of benefit to the client. This "value judgment" is based on the fact that most agencies cannot handle all of a child's problems in every case. Referrals represent an attempt to extend the operation of the agency. At the very least, according to our ideal type, there should not be biases in the giving of referrals. Biases which exist concerning where the person is sent or the socio-personal characteristics of the person represent inconsistencies in the complex organization formed by the operation of agencies focusing on community health. Where there is bias on the follow-up of referral by the client, we see the combined influence of the social organization of the community and the structural organization of the agencies of the community.

These questions are raised at this point to illustrate the kinds of judgments which are possible from the interagency description. Many similar judgments are possible: why is there so little contact between various health agencies overall? Should there be more interagency cooperation?

Other questions worthy of investigation were also raised by these data. We have found, for example, that different referral routes are used by the health and welfare clients. Two alternative "explanations" are available. The first has to do with the procedures employed by the two departments and suggests that these agencies consistently use distinctive "policies" concerning referrals. An alternative suggests that there are real differences between the type of clients who seek medical assistance through the departments. This latter hypothesis suggests that the impoverished, for example, initially seek help at the Welfare Department and, because of their poverty, must stay in the state supported system. This alternative suggests that the image held by the population concerning various departments and agencies is a worthy topic for research.

Any attempt to examine the hypothesis that different populations used different channels of referral would require gathering information from agency files. The researcher should appraise carefully the legally required channels and differentiate them from those based on policy. It is known, for instance, that in North Carolina the Welfare Department must initiate action for the placement of children in state institutions. Other similar channels are likely to exist in other states.

Another provocative finding was that multiply handicapped children do not tend to be given many more referrals than singly handicapped children; when they are given referrals they tend to be to private hospitals and not to state agencies. Furthermore, persons with multiple handicaps tend to follow up referrals less than singly handicapped children. This web of findings suggests that the parents of the multiply handicapped child know the child is not receiving the aid he deserves. Research should attempt to establish whether or not the multiply handicapped child is receiving equitable treatment compared with other children. If he is not, this might be because of restrictive and inadequate definition of the scope and domain of agencies. This hypothesis seems to warrant investigation.

In summary, it has been shown that extra-logical factors do predict to the referral patterns of health agencies. It should be pointed out again, that agencies do not operate by themselves but in terms of their organization with one another in the community. The fact that this organization is often not explicitly stated does not mean that it is non-existent. Not only do the agencies create an organizational network but they operate within a social structure. There is need for further research into the nature of clients and referral chains for health and welfare departments and into the special problems posed by children with multiple handicaps.

HOUSEHOLD SURVEYS

THE SECOND MAJOR information source tapped by the Study was that composed of the parents of the children of Alamance County. These parents are responsible for the care and well being of their children; they are responsible for seeking the kinds of help needed by the handicapped child. As society has designated them to be the most responsible persons for the care of children, it was appropriate that they be asked about how they perceive their children's needs.

It was necessary to develop a specific questionnaire designed to tap the area of parental concern. The questionnaire had to be simple yet inclusive. It was to be administered by volunteer workers so as to demonstrate that communities could, with a bit of professional help, carry on research efforts designed to provide basic data for planning.

It was necessary to recruit volunteer workers, to get laymen in Alamance County to do the job of canvassing the parents of children who were normal and handicapped. Recruiting volunteers was not an easy task but, by trial and error, volunteers were found. They completed their job adequately and the study owes much to them. Several recommendations about the conduct of health surveys are made in this section as a result of our experiences.

In the fall of 1963, a year and a half after the work in the field at Alamance had ceased, we carried on a similar household survey in Halifax County. This replication of the effort was designed to test the recommendations made concerning recruitment of volunteers as well as to provide insight into what the health needs in other counties might be like. Several interesting comparisons between the survey rates in the two counties are provided.

Parents are greatly concerned about their children. Almost half of the children reported on by parents were the objects of chronic medical concern. Undoubtedly some of this concern is not medically sound: parents tend to be over-anxious about children in our society. Yet, when the results of the questionnaires were tested in the clinic examinations—discussed later—it was found that some basis for the parental concern was present in fully 75 per cent of cases. The large disparity between the clinically adjusted rates and the survey rates is due to the fact that the adjusted rates presented earlier include *only* those conditions judged to be moderately to severely disabling.

Our data show that volunteer workers and various community organizations can profitably be utilized in attempts at providing a variety of services to a community's children.

CHAPTER VI

INTERVIEWER RESPONSE BIAS*

Can volunteer workers be recruited to conduct a health survey in a community like Alamance? If volunteers are found, can they be trained to do the job adequately? How do such volunteers compare with other workers in conducting a health survey? These are some of the questions with which the study was faced when the decision to use volunteers was made.

The recruitment, training and performance of volunteer workers are matters of great concern to those who would conduct morbidity surveys. It is not simply a matter of money but a matter of obtaining community involvement in the project. This is important because volunteer workers represent, we feel, a segment of the population who can help in resolving the community's problems if their interest can be focused.

The problem of obtaining volunteer interviewers was a formidable one. Personal efforts on the part of the staff of the Child Health Survey were, for the most part, ineffective in securing the cooperation desired. Through trial and error it was found that the most effective method of getting volunteer interviewers was to work through the formal and informal agencies dealing with medical problems: examples were the medical auxiliaries, service leagues, and community councils, most of which were found to be predominantly urban organizations. The personal persuasiveness of individual community leaders seemed to be the crucial factor. These community leaders, once persuaded, were able to command the services of a group of very select people. In this way, services of the active leaders and their associates were secured. We found that volunteers recruited from the more active agencies are likely to be already engaged in various community projects. Hence, they must be given adequate advance notice of when they are scheduled to do the interviewing. In addition, they should be given an accurate and detailed description of what the task will involve.

Once the cooperation of a group of volunteers was obtained it became evident that they were being asked to do something which many of them had never done before and for which they seemed to feel

* Original article appeared in the July, 1964, issue of the *American Journal of Public Health*. Copyright 1964, by the American Public Health Association, Inc.

themselves ill prepared. Their concern centered around a fear of being rebuffed by the people they were to interview and their inability to obtain the type of information desired. The staff sought to reduce their fears by recounting episodes of their own personal experiences. It turned out later that these anticipated situations almost never occurred: only one refusal was encountered by the volunteer staff. Our finding was, also, that even with an explanation that they were to do interviewing, most were stunned by the demand that they take nine hours of instruction in interviewing technique in addition to their field time. It is possible that the prospect of extended time commitment may have served to screen out the less qualified and less dedicated of the group, although there were very few who fell into this category.

Interviewer training was split into three sessions, each with its special area of instruction. The first session placed emphasis on the practical nature of the interview as an instrument for getting information. The second session concerned the specific interview schedule to be used in the study with emphasis on definitions and the phrasing of the questions. Stressed also was the fact that the survey was interested in parental concern rather than the clinical diagnoses which had been given to the parents. The third training session covered the practical questions of area location for each interviewer, the techniques involved in the split-interval method of area sampling, and the method of turning in completed interviews. After this training, the question remained as to how well the volunteers would compare with other interviewers who had "extra" knowledge, training and experiences. They were to be compared with social workers, registered nurses and professional interviewers.

In addition to preparing the volunteer interviewers in these ways, the staff also prepared the community for the survey. The study was granted a great deal of newspaper space, the Burlington *Times-News* maintained periodical coverage during the entire survey period. The two local radio stations donated spot announcements and editorial time to the survey. These sources constantly urged cooperation with the interviewers and with the study in general. The volunteers got feedback concerning these appeals. In the rural areas, the radio appeals were far more effective in informing the people of the survey than the newspaper.

Methodology

Success in interviewing is generally measured in terms of (1) the coverage in terms of completed interviews; (2) the representativeness of the same in terms of its characteristics; (3) the lack of interviewer response bias; and (4) the validity of the response. Presented here are data concerning the first three aspects. The validity of the responses is a separate study in itself.

The volunteers' success in terms of coverage is presented in Table 20. No statistically significant differences exist between the type of interviewer and the proportion of non-response, refusals, and non-locates.

TABLE 20

Outcome of the Interview Situation by
Type of Interviewer

Type of Interviewer	Interviews Completed	Reported Vacancy	Refused	No Contact	Total
Volunteer interviewer	787	25	1	53	866
Social worker	43	4	0	2	49
Registered nurse	135	7	1	19	162
Professional interviewer	67	2	0	9	78

$x^2 = 16.45$, NS p $>$ .05 9 degrees of freedom.

TABLE 21

Population Characteristics of Alamance County: Estimated and Sampled

Characteristic	Census Figure Adjusted to March 1962	Survey	Percent of Adjusted Population
Total Population	89,100	4,010	4.50
Males	43,500	1,945	4.47
Females	45,600	2,065	4.52
White	73,900	3,371	4.56
Negro	15,200	639	4.20
Population under 21	36,500	1,684	4.61
Males	18,600	852	4.58
Females	17,900	832	4.64
White	29,500	1,343	4.55
Negro	7,400	341	4.61
Ages 0-4	9,700	443	4.57
Ages 5-9	9,600	453	4.72
Ages 10-14	8,900	427	4.80
Ages 15-20	8,300	362	4.36

The volunteers' performance in terms of representativeness of the sample drawn is presented in Table 21. The interviewers were fairly successful in drawing a 5 per cent sample of the population. Had the study been able to devote more time to the interviews, it is possible that the theoretical sampling ratio of 5 per cent might have been reached. As it was, they were forced to complete approximately twenty interviews in a maximum of two weeks. The staff insisted on this speed in order to complete the survey phase and go on to the clinic phase before the end of the school year.

Table 22A gives the questions asked in the survey which were directed at specific handicapping conditions.

Table 22B presents the actual rates of yield for each question by the type of interviewer for the thirteen broad diagnostic categories. Chi-square values were computed on the complete distribution of

TABLE 22A

Questions Used in the Child Health Survey
by Diagnostic Category

ORTHOPEDIC

(1) Does . . . have cerebral palsy, multiple sclerosis, muscular dystrophy or other similar conditions?

(2) Has . . . ever had any paralysis of any kind, or had poor use of his legs, arms, feet, hands, or fingers?

(3) Has . . . ever had any repeated trouble with his back or spine, or any permanent stiffness or deformity of the foot, leg, arm, fingers, or back?

(4) Is . . . missing any fingers, hand or arm, toes, foot or leg, or does he have a club foot or deformed hand, regardless of the amount of correction or care?

(5) Has . . . ever had any trouble with his balance or coordination or does he ever have any jerking or twitching in his arms, legs, hands, face or other part of the body?

EPILEPSY

(6) Has . . . ever been known to suffer from epilepsy (no matter how well it is now treated or controlled)?

(7) Has . . . had more than one convulsion, fit, or spell in his life?

(8) Has . . . had any convulsions, fits, or spells after he was three years old?

VISION

(9) Has . . . ever had frequent crossings, rolling or twitching of the eyeball (not the eyelid)?

(10) Has . . . ever had serious trouble seeing without glasses?

(11) Has . . . ever had serious trouble seeing even when wearing glasses?

HEARING

(12) Is . . . hard of hearing or is he suspected of having hearing trouble?

(13) Does . . . suffer from deafness or serious trouble with hearing or does he presently use an aid to hearing?

CLEFT PALATE

(14) Does . . . have a harelip or cleft palate, regardless of the amount of correction or care?

EMOTIONAL

(15) Does . . . ever have violent temper outbursts which he is not able to control or does he ever have spells when he stares straight ahead, drops things, or falls down without reasons?

(16) Does . . . ever act peculiarly or not quite right, or does he often have a lot of difficulty in getting along with other children (or people)?

(17) Has anyone like the doctor, school teacher, minister or some other responsible person ever felt that . . . has personality trouble or trouble getting along with people?

SPEECH

(18) Has . . . ever had any speech defect or serious trouble speaking (even though it might have been corrected) ?

(19) Does . . . lisp, use baby talk, or talk in any way that is not right for his age?

MENTAL RETARDATION

(20) Was . . . unusually late in learning to sit up?

(21) Was . . . unusually late in beginning to walk?

(22) Is . . . seriously behind other children his age in any way?

(23) Is . . . mentally retarded or slow witted, or does he have serious difficulty in learning or remembering things?

CHRONIC RESPIRATORY

(24) Does . . . ever suffer from constant or chronic bronchitis, coughing, asthma, sinus trouble, or hay fever?

(25) Does . . . ever suffer from shortness of breath?

(26) How many chest colds has . . . had during the past year? (yes equals 5 or more)

(27) Does . . . usually cough up matter when he first gets up in the morning?

HEART

(28) Has . . . ever had or been suspected of having rheumatic fever?

(29) Has . . . ever been diagnosed as having heart trouble?

ORTHODONTIC

(30) Does . . . have an obvious jaw deformity?

(31) (If over 6 years) Do . . . 's teeth fail to come together for proper chewing or are they very crooked?

SKIN

(32) Has . . . ever had any serious trouble with skin rashes, exzema or acne or similar skin trouble?

(33) Does . . . have any unsightly birthmark, discoloration of the skin or other skin deformity?

(34) Has . . . ever suffered from serious trouble with boils or carbuncles or a like skin trouble?

responses including a category of "unsure," which is not shown. For most questions there is no evidence of interviewer response bias. The few questions which showed response bias seemed to be question-specific rather than category-specific. However, all the questions aimed at eliciting chronic skin conditions proved to have significant interviewer response bias. High response rates characterized the nurses and professional interviewers whereas lower rates characterized the volunteers. The actual rate of prevalence for skin conditions is, of course, not known but reported prevalence rates should not have differed so widely by type of interviewer. A similar bias also exists for chronic respiratory conditions. For the question on the number of chest colds per year, the significant variation occurred in the range of under five colds per year, which was used as the cutting point for the index of a chronic condition and is thus not shown. From an examination of the questions themselves, it seems that a possible cause for each of the significant differences might have been the unwillingness of the interviewer to ask the question of the

TABLE 22B

Rates of Yield by Question and by Type of Interviewer
Showing the Significance of Interviewer Bias

PERCENTAGE POSITIVE RESPONSE

Question Number	Volunteer (N = 1,245)	Social Worker (N = 86)	Registered Nurse (N = 192)	Professional Interviewer (N = 161)	Chi-Square and Significance*
(1)	0.6	0.0	0.0	0.6	1.68 NS
(2)	2.5	1.2	3.1	0.0	5.05 NS
(3)	2.5	0.0	7.3	3.1	23.74 S.01
(4)	0.6	0.0	0.5	1.9	3.53 NS
(5)	2.3	0.0	1.0	1.9	3.20 NS
(6)	0.3	0.0	0.5	1.0	7.40 NS
(7)	2.4	1.2	3.1	3.1	1.16 NS
(8)	1.3	1.2	2.9	3.8	6.72 NS
(9)	1.5	2.3	2.6	1.2	1.51 NS
(10)	11.0	16.3	11.8	13.7	2.68 NS
(11)	0.4	0.0	0.0	1.6	4.74 NS
(12)	2.5	5.8	2.6	5.6	7.91 NS
(13)	0.7	0.0	0.5	0.0	1.96 NS
(14)	0.1	0.0	0.0	0.0	0.34 NS
(15)	1.1	1.2	1.6	2.5	2.68 NS
(16)	1.2	3.5	0.5	5.0	16.22 S.01
(17)	1.3	2.3	1.1	2.5	1.82 NS
(18)	4.9	6.0	4.3	9.3	6.10 NS
(19)	2.4	7.1	2.2	4.4	8.18 NS
(20)	2.2	1.2	1.1	3.8	4.82 NS
(21)	3.5	3.5	2.7	5.0	2.47 NS
(22)	4.6	1.2	1.1	6.8	10.20 NS
(23)	3.0	2.4	3.2	3.1	1.33 NS
(24)	12.6	8.1	15.6	14.3	3.19 NS
(25)	3.7	4.7	4.7	3.1	0.83 NS
(26)	1.3	1.2	0.6	1.3	2.19 NS**
(27)	2.9	3.5	4.3	9.3	16.93 S.01
(28)	1.9	1.2	2.6	0.6	2.02 NS
(29)	1.4	1.2	2.6	1.9	1.68 NS
(30)	0.1	0.0	0.0	0.0	0.34 NS
(31)	4.7	4.7	4.6	7.7	1.89 NS
(32)	7.1	8.1	14.1	17.5	26.07 S.01
(33)	4.6	3.5	6.8	10.6	11.41 S.01
(34)	1.9	4.7	7.4	2.5	19.56 S.01

　* Significance levels are indicated: NS means not statistically significant at less than the .05 level; S.05 means significant at less than the .05 level; S.01 means significant at less than the .01 level.
　** Recomputed with 5 or more as cut-off point.

respondent. For example, the question: "Does . . . usually cough up matter when he first gets up in the morning?" Positive responses were more frequent for interviewers who had previous experience asking questions of this nature in a routine manner; for example, nurses. An alternative hypothesis may be advanced to explain bias for other questions: that of specific interests and concerns. Such a factor may be operative in producing response bias to the question: "Does . . . ever act peculiarly or not quite right, or does he often have a lot of difficulty in getting along with other children (or people)?" Here, social workers, who are closely involved with this sort of problem, elicited higher response rates than nurses, whose interests tend more toward physical problems. If this explanation holds true, its converse would help explain the bias existing in the question: "Has . . . ever had any repeated trouble with his back or spine, or any permanent stiffness or deformity of foot, leg, arm, fingers, or back?" These two types of possible "explanation" are offered to "explain" the response bias existing in this study.

Discussion

From this study there seems to be no statistical evidence to reject the hypothesis that volunteer interviewers can be used in morbidity surveys. The Hunterdon study was also willing to accept the value of volunteer enumerators.[1] In the present study, for most questions, the volunteers elicited a medium rate of response without the heightened response rate for specificities shown by enumerators with special interests. Thus, when using volunteers, the only caution is that it may be necessary to use carefully worded questions to probe sensitive areas. Whereas adequate training should always be given, there is evidence that even this training is powerless to reduce the specific interests of strongly biased persons. Response bias, where it exists, seems to be reflected in over-valuing some reports and under-valuing others. Volunteers seem to be fairly free of these specific interests. Thus, aside from the cost factor, this consistency of response is a strong point in favor of the use of volunteer interviewers while their presumed hesitation to ask some noxious questions might be a point against their employment.

It is probably true that the success of these interviewers was in no small way due to their personal characteristics. All were the wives of professional or sales personnel in the community. Of the 58 women, only three had not completed four years of college or nursing school. Several had Master's degrees and twenty per cent of them had training and experience in education. They had, on the average, two children. Five were the mothers of handicapped children.

One latent function of the interviewing experience for these workers was that the interviewing was a learning situation and the interviewers undoubtedly profited from it. Many of these women were exposed to medical, social, and legal questions which would otherwise have been outside their experience. Certainly one can conceive of

1. Commission on Chronic Illness, Chronic Illness in a Rural Area. Cambridge, Mass.: Harvard University Press, 1959.

these women becoming concerned and active in this area as a direct result of their training and experience in interviewing.

What general principles for getting volunteers can this study discern from its efforts? First, let the community leaders select their own interviewers. This is necessary because the community leaders wield the power necessary to make the persons comply with the request and because it is through this channel that one is able to get to the elite of the community. Second, allow enough time for the volunteers to fit the new task into their already busy schedules. If one wants the capable people, expect them to be active in other community affairs; the only way to get around refusal because of their heavy commitments is to allow them ample time to integrate the new task into their existing schedules. Third, expect that the workers will want and demand some knowledge of the results of their efforts. The study directors should be prepared to supply the workers with satisfactory information as a reward for their participation. Indeed, this staff has been hard pressed to comply with the demand for information revealed by their survey of the handicapped child in Alamance County.

In summary, volunteer interviewers, as far as this study was able to discern, can be used in morbidity surveys if they are recruited through the informal social service structure of the community. In this manner the aid of an elite and dedicated group of workers can be assured, and workers with high personal qualifications are essential to success of the undertaking. The only recommendation that can be made, other than to insure adequate training, would be in the area of the schedule design. Here, it may prove necessary to probe sensitive areas with carefully worded questions.

However, it is not sufficient to say as a result of this study that volunteers may be successfully used in morbidity surveys. Of equal importance is a consideration of why they should be used. Their use has a number of positive values. From the budgetary aspect it can reduce the cost of a survey to the point where it is a feasible operation. From the standpoint of reliability the volunteers had a medium rate of response with no one-sided emphasis. From the aspect of presumed validity it increases the consumer confidence in his data. From the view of public interest and community involvement it makes the community feel that this is *their* project rather than something imposed on them. From the personal education standpoint it lets the informal leaders of the community see the existing conditions of their community. Thus, the finding that volunteer interviewers are relatively free of response bias compared to other professional workers may have many practical implications for future research.

CHAPTER VII

ALAMANCE AND HALIFAX COUNTIES

The experience with the household survey in Alamance County suggested that other communities might, with a modicum of professional assistance, be able to use this method of securing morbidity information regarding handicapping conditions in children which would be useful in planning community services and facilities. This suggestion involved two assumptions which are, realistically, in need of further investigation: (1) that volunteer workers could be recruited to conduct the survey; and (2) that the morbidity rates generated in another county would be sufficiently comparable to provide a reliable and satisfactory basis for community planning.

In the fall of 1963 the decision was made to test these assumptions in Halifax County. Work in Halifax County began in September, 1963 and the final report concerning these efforts was submitted in February, 1964. In this we have demonstrated that the information can be obtained in a relatively short period of time and at minimum cost. The question now becomes, "Was it worth the effort?" Was the information obtained useful and was it reliable?

As has been noted, Alamance County is a highly industrialized, urban, rapidly growing county in the central Piedmont of North Carolina. By contrast Halifax County is in the coastal region of the state; its economy is typically rural, small farming. Whereas Alamance County is growing, the population of Halifax County is declining. The percentage of Negro population in Alamance County is 17 while in Halifax it is 55 per cent. In Alamance County in 1959, per capita income was $1,800 and in Halifax, $1,491. Per capita income for non-white families in Alamance was $659, and in Halifax for that same year it was $342. Median education in years for Alamance was 10.2 for whites and 7.1 for Negroes; in Halifax, the corresponding figures are 9.3 and 5.4. As these data show, there were real differences between the two counties. The question became, how do these parents compare in their awareness of medical problems?

Volunteer Participation In Halifax County

The Halifax County Health Department accepted the idea of the household survey enthusiastically and assumed responsibility for recruiting the volunteers both directly and through the cooperation of some of the voluntary health organizations in the county. It turned out that one of these organizations which promised a large number of volunteers provided but two and the number of volunteers enlisted by the Health Department staff and other agencies was not sufficient. In this, the recruiting of volunteers in Halifax County was something of a failure because the Department relied on the optimistic promises of a single voluntary health organization. While the study staff was somewhat concerned by the optimism of a single health organization, it was decided not to interfere with the Department's planning. When it became evident that the volunteers were not going to be able to complete the required number of interviews, a five per cent sample of the county, the Health Director offered the assistance of his public health nurses, and eight nurses completed the data-gathering phase.

In retrospect, there are two factors which may have entered into the problem of insufficient volunteers. In the first place the study staff did not enter at all into the recruiting drive. Without partici- pating directly in enlistment, it might have aided by consulting more closely with the Health Department staff. In other words, it might have been anticipated that a community would require different approaches. In the second place, Halifax County tends to be divided into discrete communities with too little tradition of common effort and communication; such a lack of communication should have been taken into account in an effort of this kind.

There were thirty-three volunteer workers in the study in Halifax County. Their average age was 36 years; two were over 50 and three were under 25. These workers had, on the average, completed high school. Two were registered nurses. The volunteers had 2.3 children and six of the workers were themselves the parents of handicapped children. Twenty-three, or 70 per cent, identified themselves as house- wives and the remainder had employment as nurses, bookkeepers, secretaries and office workers. The majority, 61 per cent, of these volunteers had to be influenced to participate by the Health Depart- ment. The women who participated in the survey were members of volunteer associations in Halifax County: they reported 45 associa- tional memberships, an average of 1.4 per worker.

These volunteer workers began their training on November 5, 1963. Each worker was to receive a minimum of nine hours training though some received less as the need for more workers became obvious. It became quite clear by the second week of training that the thirty-three participants could not complete the estimated 720 interviews, the five per cent sample of the households. Several of the workers limited their interviews to the ten they had been told would be required of them. It is probably unwise to estimate prematurely the number of interviews each worker is expected to complete.

In Alamance County it was planned that workers other than volunteers be used: professional interviewers, social workers and nurses conducted a portion of the survey in order to test the idea that volunteers could do an adequate job of conducting a survey of this kind. It may always be wise to have some professional people available to supplement the basic volunteer staff if that becomes necessary.

In Halifax County the study staff tested the idea that the community itself could be relied on to conduct a study of this kind. The assistance given to the Health Department staff was minimal: some encouragement, some offers to assist, a bit of help with publicity, and one lecturer was supplied to address a meeting of clubwomen who might participate. It is probably unrealistic to expect that this minimum is sufficient. At least in the case of Halifax County, our experiences suggest that participation in the recruiting drive by persons trained in recruiting should be provided.

In addition to judging the success of the drive by means of the numbers of volunteers obtained, several additional criteria of the entire attempt at recruiting are important. The first of these concerns the contacting of the correct number of households and the second, the bias displayed by the volunteers in the eliciting of responses.

The survey of households in Halifax County aimed at a 5 per cent sample of the population. The materials presented in Table 23 indicate that this goal was not attained. There is no reason to believe, however, that the data obtained by the workers in Halifax were biased in terms of the sample. The sample is a smaller one than that which was desired: the confidence limits surrounding the estimates are larger than those which were desired. It would still appear to be a random, four per cent, sample of the households.

The failure to obtain completed interviews with the full five per cent of the county seemed to be the result of the failure of the public health nurses to contact their assigned families. This means that during the three interviewing days in which the nurses worked, they were not able to make repeated callbacks at the homes to which they were assigned. During the two week period in which the volunteers

TABLE 23

A Comparison of the 1960 Census Figures for Halifax County and the
Household Survey of the County

	1960 Census	Survey	Per Cent of Population 1960
Total Population	58,956	2,357	4.0
Males	28,969	1,156	4.0
Females	29,987	1,201	4.0
White	26,492	1,056	4.0
Negro	32,464	1,301	4.0
Population Under 21	28,694	1,229	4.3
0- 4 years	7,449	328	4.4
5- 9 years	7,673	305	4.0
10-14 years	7,427	321	4.3
15-20 years	6,145	275	4.5
Males	14,413	629	4.4
Females	14,281	600	4.2
White	9,996	437	4.4
Negro	18,698	792	4.0

worked, repeated efforts to contact homes where no response was
elicited initially were possible; in the three days the nurses worked,
this calling back time and time again could not profitably be
completed.

Presented in Table 24 are the outcomes of the interview situation
by type of interviewer. It is seen that the nurses completed an average
of 17.8 interviews while the volunteer workers completed 12.3. The
nurses worked for three days, full time, to collect their interviews
while the volunteers had as long as two weeks to complete their
assignments.

TABLE 24

Outcome of the Interview Situation by Type of Interviewer,
Nurses and Volunteers — Halifax Household Survey

	No. Interviewers	Completed	Reported Vacancy	Refusal	No Contact	Total
Nurses	8	143	30	2	26	201
Volunteers	33	405	39	2	21	467
Totals	41	548	69	4	47	668

$\chi^2 = 25.237$ p less than .001.

The Chi-square value of 25.24, significant at the .001 level, indicates that the nurses differed from the volunteer workers with
regard to interviews completed. This difference in outcome is most
marked in the categories "reported vacancy" and "no contact." The
nurses, in their few days of interviewing, reported a larger proportion
of vacancies and were unable to locate a larger proprotion of residents
of the apparently occupied homes in the areas to which they were

assigned. The nurses, pressed as they were for time, could not make the necessary repeated callbacks.

In any case, the fact of not planning for a sufficient number of volunteers had its consequences on the data collected: in hastily using available public health nurses, the study was forced to accept the probability of a hurried job: the inevitable result was an increase in the failures to locate families who were hard to find. In part compensating for this may be the fact that families with children— the families in which the study was most concerned—were the more easily located: families with children are probably more apt to be at home than families without children.

With regard to the second criterion of adequacy mentioned above, that of interviewer response bias, four questions were found to elicit different rates of response when asked by nurses and by volunteer workers. These questions were: No. 6. Has . . . ever been known to suffer from epilepsy? (no matter how well it is now treated or controlled.); No. 10. Has . . . ever had serious trouble seeing without glasses? No. 24. Does . . . ever suffer from constant or chronic bronchitis, coughing, asthma, sinus trouble or hay fever? No. 35. Does . . . have anything wrong with him at all that you know of and that we have not asked about? These questions each had statistically different response rates for the nurses and the volunteers. These differences are presented in Table 25.

TABLE 25

Rates of Yield by Question and by Type of Interviewer,
Showing the Significance of Interviewer Bias—Halifax Household Survey

PERCENTAGE POSITIVE

Question No.	Volunteers (N = 405)	Nurses (N = 143)	Chi-Square Significance
6	.1	1.4	8.81 S.01
10	8.4	5.1	4.01 S.05
24	5.6	9.9	7.48 S.01
35	5.3	8.5	4.65 S.05

For three of these four questions, Nos. 6, 24 and 35 the nurses elicited more positive replies from respondents than did the volunteer workers. And only for No. 10 did the volunteers elicit more positive responses. An admittedly *post hoc* explanation stems from a familiarity with the work done by nurses: they are charged with responsibility for checking the eyesight of many of the school children in the county. They are "experts" in that field.

None of these were questions showing differences in the original study of response bias, cited in the previous chapter. Of course, in

Alamance County, the differences were reported for four categories of interviewers and the present instance focuses on differences between nurses and volunteers only.

On the basis of the clinical experiences in Alamance County, reported in detail in a later chapter, it was found that questions No. 10 and No. 24 tended to overreport normal children. In a study of the clinical validity of these questions, No. 10 and No. 24 brought too many false positives into the clinic—children who were clinically normal but whose parents responded positively.

Question 6, on the other hand, brought into the clinic many children who, though not epileptics, did have some condition in which the study was interested, emotional disturbance and mental retardation.

Results In Halifax County: Morbidity

Information was obtained in the completed interviews on 1,229 persons under 21 years of age. Of these, 759 or 62 per cent, were reported to be completely normal by their parents. The parents of 431 other children reported a total of 686 presumptively handicapping conditions, an average of 1.6 per child. The remaining 76 children were reported to be afflicted with conditions other than the 13 conditions with which this study primarily deals. In sum, then, 38 per cent of the children in the survey population are reported to be presumptively handicapped. The usual practice is not to report numbers of handicapped children but rates of handicapping conditions per thousand, so the data presented in Table 26 are the rates of handicapping conditions per thousand of population under 21 as reported by means of the household survey of the county.

These data suggest that in terms of sheer numbers of children, parental concern is greatest in the areas of chronic skin conditions, chronic respiratory problems, vision difficulties and mental retardation, in that order. Parental concern with and recognition of difficulties tend to increase with the age of the children. The highest rates of handicapping conditions are reported for the 15 to 20 year age category. This direct relationship with age is most clear for orthopedic conditions, vision difficulties and mental retardation.

The rates of handicapping conditions for males and females, overall, are approximately the same. However, this average is similar only because of inequities in rates for specific conditions. Significantly more males are reported to have orthopedic problems, speech

TABLE 26

Prevalence Rates Per 1,000 Persons Under 21 of Presumptively Handicapping Conditions by Selected Social and Demographic Characteristics: Halifax County Household Survey, November, 1963

Presumptive Diagnosis	Total Sample	Age				Sex		Race		Social Class		
		0-4	5-9	10-14	15-20	Male	Female	White	Negro	Upper & Middle	Working	Lower
Any handicap	620	415	639	717	731	626	613	700	575	578	668	605
Orthopedic conditions	49	27	53	37	84	59	38	50	48	45	58	45
Epilepsy	23	24	20	22	25	22	23	23	23	21	36	13
Vision defects	89	21	59	134	149	67	112	98	83	83	116	70
Hearing defects	20	6	30	22	22	21	18	21	19	24	17	19
Cleft palate	4	6	7	3	...	3	5	2	5	3	...	8
Emotional disturbance	26	12	43	34	15	25	27	25	27	24	19	32
Speech disorders	53	52	56	44	62	67	38	41	59	32	46	68
Mental retardation	77	43	92	87	87	85	67	62	85	49	56	108
Respiratory disorders	90	70	92	103	95	100	78	133	66	97	114	66
Heart conditions	9	3	10	9	15	5	13	18	4	11	15	4
Orthodontic conditions	27	3	36	50	18	19	35	34	23	28	24	28
Cerebral palsy	...	...	...	...	...	...	...	...	...	...	...	...
Skin conditions	94	106	92	81	95	89	98	105	87	94	104	85
Other	62	40	53	90	66	64	60	87	48	63	65	59

Total *number of children* with some handicap = 431.

difficulties and mental retardation. More females are reported to have conditions in the areas of vision, orthodontic and heart conditions.

A greater proportion of white parents report their children as afflicted with these handicapping conditions than do Negro parents. With regard to specific conditions, more white parents see their offspring as troubled with chronic respiratory conditions, heart difficulties, orthodontic problems and skin conditions. A greater proportion of Negro parents report their children to be mentally retarded, to have speech problems, and to have cleft palate.

Those families estimated to be in the working class in Halifax County reported more handicapping conditions in their children than those families estimated to be upper or middle class, or lower class.

Comparison of Alamance and Halifax Counties By Survey Rates

There were differences between the household survey rates generated in these two North Carolina counties. These rates are presented in Table 27. Testing the significance of these differences, there is a variance ratio of 9.49, with 1 and 16 degrees of freedom, which is significant at less than the .01 level.

TABLE 27
Morbidity Rate per 1,000 Persons Under 21 in Two North Carolina Counties as Reported by Household Surveys

Condition	Alamance County	Halifax County
Orthopedic conditions	63	49
Epilepsy	31	23
Vision defects	126	89
Hearing defects	30	20
Cleft palate	0.7	4
Emotional disturbance	30	26
Speech disorders	64	53
Mental retardation	79	77
Respiratory disorders	163	90
Heart conditions	27	9
Orthodontic conditions	35	27
Cerebral palsy	5	....
Skin conditions	148	94
Other	105	62
Number in each sample	1,684	1,229

The data here indicate that, in general, morbidity is reported less frequently for the children of Halifax than for those of Alamance County. The most noticeable differences between these rates occur for vision defects, chronic respiratory conditions, heart conditions, skin conditions and "other" handicaps. The first four of these conditions, it should be noted, are those with the least clinical validation in the Alamance County survey. In an effort to pinpoint some of the factors influencing the rates reported by the parents of these counties, morbidity is described in terms of rather obvious demographic indices: race, sex, social class and age.

Race. The factor of race is highly significant in determining morbidity rates as reported by parents. These data for the two counties are presented in Table 28. Several rather clear differences are notable: in Alamance County, Negro families tend to report morbidity at the same rate or higher than the white families, while in Halifax, the rates are consistently the same rates as white families or lower. This trend is most notable for vision, chronic respiratory, skin conditions and orthodontic conditions.

TABLE 28

Morbidity Rate per 1,000 Persons Under 21 in Two North Carolina
Counties by Race as Reported by Household Surveys

| | Alamance County | | Halifax County | |
Condition	White	Negro	White	Negro
Orthopedic conditions	64	60	50	48
Epilepsy	33	27	23	23
Vision defects	121	197	98	83
Hearing defects	26	48	21	19
Cleft palate	1	....	2	5
Emotional disturbance	24	54	25	27
Speech disorders	55	87	41	59
Mental retardation	65	141	62	85
Respiratory disorders	148	225	138	66
Heart conditions	27	30	18	4
Orthodontic conditions	30	57	34	23
Cerebral palsy	6	3	....	....
Skin conditions	133	213	105	87
Other	108	84	87	48
Number in each sample	1,343	341	437	792

It would appear that the differences between the two counties could be accounted for in terms of the different morbidity rates generated by the Negroes in the two counties. Certainly the differences between the white families in the two counties are less disparate than the differences between the two Negro family rates.

Sex. In Alamance County, in general, more males were described as handicapped than females and, to a lesser extent, the same thing holds for Halifax. Whatever factors influence parents in describing morbid conditions seems to affect the judgments made concerning males more than females. This does not mean, however, that for all conditions males have a rate of morbidity greater than that reported for females: females in both counties are reported to have vision difficulties, heart conditions, orthodontic difficulties and skin conditions at rates higher than males.

Social Class. In Alamance County, morbidity is inversely related to social class: as one goes down the social class scale, morbidity rates increase. In Halifax, on the other hand, the working class reports the highest morbidity. It would appear that with respect to whatever values affect the parents' responses to questions, the working class in Halifax is most like the lower class in Alamance County. Perhaps this is a reflection of a lower level of medical sophistication or awareness.

Age. In Alamance and Halifax counties, the rates of morbidity tend to increase with age. This direct relationship is most evident for vision defects and chronic respiratory conditions.

Discussion

One possible explanation of the disparities between the two counties is that they are due to errors in measurement, attributable either to use of the schedule or to interviewer error. It appears unlikely that such errors account for a significant part of the observed differences. The differences, therefore, probably reflect very real social differences between the counties.

This suggestion brings us right back to one of the major purposes of this study: specification of the relationship between the handicapped child and the society of which he is a part. It was pointed out earlier that the household survey measured the problems of handicapping according to parents. That is to say, it is a measure of the awareness and concern of parents with reference to possibly handicapping conditions which their children may have. Awareness and concern are a reflection of many things: definite diagnoses which have been given by physicians or other professional persons, the parent's feeling of concern as the mark of a "good parent," his individual level of "health anxiety," and, of special significance to our inquiry, social and cultural values of the community or group of which the family is a part. Among social groups in which less emphasis has been placed on the well-being of the individual, in which there is toleration of wider departures from health norms, or in which a larger proportion of the group suffer from handicapping conditions, the less disabling conditions might be expected to attract less attention and to be less frequently reported. On the other hand, even in such groups the more severe conditions, such as cleft palate, severe mental retardations, or severe orthopedic deformity, would be recognized and reported.

From the differences which have already been described between Alamance and Halifax Counties—the higher proportion of Negro population, the lower educational level and per capita income in

Halifax and the absence in Halifax of a single central community in which the economic, governmental and social influences of the county are focused—it is reasonable to suggest that the Negroes of Halifax County have a lower awareness of the milder handicapping or potentially handicapping conditions than those of Alamance, and that this is a major factor in the differences between the rates generated by the two surveys.

Generalizing from this suggestion, it is possible to advance a hypothesis with regard to morbidity rates reported from household surveys that the more industrialized, better educated, higher-income the area, the higher will be its family-reported morbidity rates.

The data available do not permit exploration of this hypothesis, but they do suggest that study of the relationship of various social and cultural factors to the recognition of medical problems is very much needed. Indeed, an understanding of these factors is vitally important to the interpretation of such morbidity data as that derived by this study and to the development of facilities and programs for meeting the full health needs of the community.

Applying The Alamance Figures To The Halifax Data

What has been said above casts some doubt on the validity of applying correction factors derived from the Alamance clinical studies to the Halifax survey data to secure an estimate of the actual prevalence rates. However, we have no better data available, nor any better estimates of the amount of over- and underreporting than those provided by the Alamance experience, and it seemed worthwhile to make these adjustments. It may be observed by comparing the final result of this adjustment process, column six of Table 30, with the comparable rates for Alamance in column six of Table 5 that, although all the Halifax estimates except that for cleft palate are lower, the order of magnitude is similar and the Halifax estimates seem to provide an adequate basis for determining the need for programs, services and facilities.

The rates estimated on the basis of the household survey in Alamance County were validated and adjusted on the basis of clinical examination of a sample of children reported as presumptively handicapped and as presumptively normal. This process provided two factors, one which corrected under- and overreporting and one that classified conditions present by degree of severity as mild, moderate and severe. It does not necessarily follow that the degree of under- and overreporting and the proportion with mild, moderate and severe handicapping is the same in Halifax as in Alamance County but it is a reasonable assumption that the two counties would, overall, show the same order of magnitude of disability. Proceeding on this assumption, the Halifax survey data have been adjusted to provide estimates of total rates. The correction factors derived from the Alamance study, and the adjusted rates are shown in Table 29.

TABLE 29

Halifax County Adjusted Rates Per 1,000 Persons Under 21 Based on
The Clinical Experience in Alamance County

Condition	Survey Rates Halifax	Correction Factor	Adjusted Rates Halifax
Orthopedic conditions	49	.952	47
Epilepsy	23	.387	9
Vision defects	89	.976	87
Hearing defects	20	1.633	33
Cleft palate	4	4.285	17
Emotional disturbance	26	3.533	92
Speech disorders	53	.718	38
Mental retardation	77	1.139	88
Respiratory disorders	90	.632	56
Heart conditions	9	2.333	21
Orthodontic conditions	27	2.542	69
Cerebral palsy	....	1.600	....
Skin conditions	94	.520	48

It is evident that statistically the smaller rates of handicapping conditions have the widest confidence limits, the widest variation. In the two cases of cerebral palsy and cleft palate, the number of children is extremely small and the confidence to be placed in these particular estimates is therefore slight. For Halifax County, the figure for cleft palate is undoubtedly too high and the figure for cerebral palsy, undoubtedly, too low.

On the questionnaire, there are no opportunities for parents to describe the severity of the conditions affecting those children. Physicians and planners are extremely interested in such estimates. A simple orthopedic difficulty may be easily treated, whereas severe cases require extensive, expensive, treatment. Again using materials gathered initially in Alamance County, it is possible to estimate the distribution of severity of each condition if one is willing to assume that the distribution in Alamance and Halifax Counties is the same. These materials are presented in Table 30.

As explained in Chapter II, these percentage distributions by severity are based on the clinical judgments of examining physicians at the Alamance County Child Health Clinic. They mean, for example, that in that clinic the orthopedists who examined all orthopedic cases found that 17 per cent of the orthopedically deformed

TABLE 30

Halifax County Adjusted Rates Per 1,000 Persons Under 21 and the
Distribution of Severity of Conditions

Condition	Adjusted Survey Rates	None	Mild	Moderate	Severe	Rates Moderate to Severe Only
Orthopedic conditions	47	17	61	17	6	11
Epilepsy	9	....	....	100	....	9
Vision defects	87	54	24	16	6	19
Hearing defects	33	24	57	19	....	6
Cleft palate	17	50	....	....	50	9
Emotional disturbance	92	....	51	38	11	45
Speech disorders	38	3	71	19	6	10
Mental retardation	88	....	15	55	30	75
Respiratory disorders	56	4	65	21	7	16
Heart conditions	21	77	17	3	3	1
Orthodontic conditions	69	...	60	37	3	28
Cerebral palsy	....	....	20	60	20	....
Skin conditions	48	14	71	14	....	7

(Above the severity columns: *Percentage Distribution by Severity*)

children were not handicapped at all; on the scale of mild, moderate and severe, these same physicians judged 61 per cent of the conditions to be mild, 17 per cent of the conditions to be moderate, and 6 per cent to be severe.

The final column in Table 30 presents the rates per thousand of population under 21 years of age with moderate to severe conditions. This estimate of prevalence is the one which is presumed to be of greatest value to planners and physicians in that: (1) this estimate concerns only those children who are definitely in need of help; (2) is a minimum estimate of the prevalence of these conditions. These minimal prevalence rates indicate that the greatest problems for the health planners of Halifax County are those of mental retardation and emotional disturbances, both areas broadly defined as "mental health."

Dental problems, vision difficulties and orthopedic difficulties also affect large numbers of children in Halifax County.

It is unfortunate that the sample of children examined in the clinic at Alamance County was so small that it is not possible to amend the total prevalence to conform to disparities by social class and race noted in an earlier section of this chapter.

Summary and Conclusions

The proposition that volunteer workers could be employed to conduct health surveys of a relatively simple type is partly substantiated by the work in Halifax County. Experience there suggests, however, that some minimum of professional assistance is necessary in the recruiting process.

Interviewer response bias is shown to exist again in the Halifax County portion of the overall study. However, this bias cannot be used to explain the major disparities between the rates generated by the survey in Halifax and those reported in Alamance County.

Assuming that the instrument employed in Alamance and Halifax Counties is reliable, it is suggested that counties displaying the greatest degree of industrialization and advantage will report the largest rates of handicapping conditions. As people become aware of ideal health, their concern increases. The clinic experience in Alamance County suggests that parental concern may be clinically verified.

While real differences between the family reported rates of morbidity do exist, it is found that the problems of concern to parents in both counties are big problems. In Halifax County fully 38 per cent of the children on whom questionnaires were completed were of parental concern.

Adjusting the figure generated in Halifax County on the basis of the Alamance County experience, it is suggested that the same sorts of problems face the two counties. Both have their greatest problems in the areas of mental health, orthodontic conditions, visual defects and chronic respiratory conditions.

CLINICAL EXAMINATIONS

EARLY IN THE STUDY it had been planned to validate the information obtained in the records and the household surveys by means of a diagnostic clinic in which subsamples of the children would be examined. It became clear very quickly that while there might be some overlap in the kinds of information obtained in files or on questionnaires and the diagnoses made by examining physicians, there would necessarily be vast differences. Medical agencies have their own ends and purposes in maintaining files and parents answer questions concerning their children for a variety of reasons. So the clinic was more than an attempt to determine morbidity; it was to become a means of understanding health practices and procedures.

PART IV

Some insight into the ways the community values health is provided in the study of clinic attendance. The study offered free, thorough work-ups to children, and yet not all who were invited came; we feel that the reasons children did not attend are related in part to differences in health awareness and values in the community.

The examinations provided a criterion, a yardstick on the basis of which it is possible to assay the medical practice of Alamance County. It was found that children who were examined in the clinic were or were not obtaining adequate care on the basis of the major disabilities afflicting the children. Further, for specific conditions, race and financial status of the family were related to the receiving of medical care.

An analogy might help in understanding the way in which this aspect of the clinic data has been interpreted: the pathologist is capable of judging the adequacy of the diagnostician; the Alamance County Child Health Clinic might be viewed as a social pathologist's study. Viewed in this way it became a method of evaluating the kinds of medical care being given in the county.

CHAPTER VIII

ATTENDANCE AT THE CLINIC*

In the area of health statistics there is increasing evidence that clinical examinations must supplement household surveys if reliable estimates are to be made of the prevalence of morbidity.[1] Studies of morbidity which have attempted to validate survey reports have encountered numerous problems, among them the refusal of some to participate in the medical examinations. The phenomenon of non-participation must be taken into account in validating health surveys; its analysis should, as Cobb, King, and Chen suggest, be a part of the basic research design.[2]

Here are the data on attendance and non-attendance at the evaluation clinic for handicapped children conducted in Alamance County in the spring and summer of 1962. The rates of attendance and reasons for non-attendance are analyzed in terms of age, sex, race, time of appointment to the clinic, source of invitation to the clinic, presumptive diagnosis, and the occupation of the head of household of the invitee.

Previous studies of clinic attendance have tended to categorize persons dichotomously into those who attended and those who did not. This simple treatment obscures the fact that there are many factors which might be expected to enter into non-participation. From the standpoint of social psychology it is possible to develop a scale of the motivation of people which would predict attendance. On another level of analysis it is possible to relate non-attendance to social categories, or to medical facts, or even to neighborhood communication patterns. This chapter attempts to understand some of the latter types of relationships by means of sociologically and medically relevant correlates of non-attendance. The motivation of non-attendance has been handled elsewhere by Chen and Cobb.[3]

---

* Original article appeared in the August, 1964, issue of the *American Journal of Public Health.* Copyright 1964, by the American Public Health Association, Inc.

1. See, for example, Barker S. Sanders, "Have Morbidity Surveys Been Oversold," *American Journal of Public Health.* 52 (October, 1962), pp. 1648-1660.

2. Sidney Cobb, Stanley King, and Edith Chen, "Differences Between Respondents and Nonrespondents in a Morbidity Survey Involving Clinical Examination," *Journal of Chronic Diseases.* 6 (August, 1957), pp. 95-107.

3. Edith Chen and Sidney Cobb, "Further Study of the Non-Participation Problems in a Morbidity Survey Involving Clinical Examination," *Journal of Chronic Diseases.* 7 (April 1958), pp. 321-331.

The Process of Invitation

The North Carolina Survey of Handicapped Children was designed to estimate morbidity rates of handicapping conditions in children under 21 years of age using three methods: records review, interview, and clinical evaluation in an intensive study of a limited geographic area. A household survey followed an extensive review of the records maintained by various medical and paramedical agencies. From these data, subsamples were drawn by presumptive diagnosis to provide clinical verification of the estimates. The sampling rates for children from the household survey varied by presumptive diagnosis from one hundred per cent of those reported to have cleft palate to one in seven of the presumptively normal children.

The invitation to the clinic consisted of a form letter addressed to the parents of the very young, and to the individual child if he was eighteen years of age or older. A stamped, self-addressed postcard was enclosed and was to be returned to the hospital if the invitation was to be accepted. No opportunity was given to refuse by mail. These invitations were mailed about one week before the scheduled date of the examination. For those who did not return the postcards, follow-up phone calls and house visits were made prior to the scheduled examinations.

There were two reasons for contacting the family of the potential non-participant. First, an attempt was made to obtain their cooperation. Second, if they were not to participate, the effort was made to ascertain the reason for not participating. In cases where cooperation could not be immediately elicited or where hostile reactions were evoked, the interviewer terminated the call. In such cases the family's private physician was asked to request the family to cooperate. Public health nurses and school teachers similarly urged cooperation.

Sometimes it was not possible to locate the invitees. As soon as the Post Office returned an invitation stamped "unknown" or "unclaimed" an interviewer went to the address and attempted to deliver the mail by hand. (This was possible in many cases because the Post Office refused to deliver mail to houses with substandard postal boxes.) In cases where the family had moved to another area or another house in Alamance County it was sometimes possible to secure the new address from neighbors at the old. Where this procedure did not produce any results, it became necessary to try to locate children through school records, through the Welfare Department, or through other agencies. Ten per cent of the total number invited could not be located by these procedures and thus were relegated to the category of "not located."

The non-located invitee to a health clinic presents two different kinds of problems to the health statistician. The first problem concerns estimating incidence of morbidity and is generally resolved by assuming that the non-located persons tend to have characteristics similar to those who are located. The second problem concerns analysis of attendance itself. It is invalid to report attendance rates at a clinic as though this category of persons did not exist.

Non-participants could be classified into other categories besides not located: those who were no longer in the sample, those who offered a valid excuse, and those who simply refused to participate. The category of those who offered a valid excuse includes those who offered excuses such as acute illness, temporary institutionalization, and temporary residence outside of the county. In such cases, other appointments were attempted. The final category of non-participation used here is that of the ones who were no longer in the sample. These are the deceased, the permanent emigrants from Alamance County and the permanently institutionalized whose institution-alization was not reported on the agency files.

The Results

Seven hundred invitations were sent to the sample of pre-sumptively handicapped children and four hundred and fifty-six examinations were completed. This represents an attendance rate of sixty-five per cent which is well within the range of rates presented by Cobb, King, and Chen.[4] The rates of attendance and reasons for non-attendance by sex and source of sample selection are presented in Table 31. There is no statistically significant difference by sex for the total sample. Differences do exist, however, for reasons for non-attendance: children whose names were drawn from the agencies have a lower rate of "excuse offering" and a higher rate of non-locatability than children sampled from the household survey. This finding is expected because the survey was completed only one month before the initial invitations to the clinic were sent; agency data, on the other hand, tend to be much older. Obtaining only current cases from agencies is almost impossible due to the specialized record keeping techniques employed by the various agencies. It is possible that the lower rate of "excuse offering" among the persons drawn

4. Sidney Cobb, Stanley King, and Edith Chen, *op. cit.*

from agency files may be related to medical experience. Under the assumption that children invited from agency records tend to experience more medical treatment, it is possible to suggest that prior medical experience is favorable to attendance.

TABLE 31

Response to Clinic Invitations by Sex and Source of Sample Selection

Sex and Source of Sample Selection	Response to Clinic Invitation			Reason for Nonattendance			
	No. of Persons	Total %	Attended	Not Located	No Longer in Sample	Excuse Offered	No Excuse Offered
Total							
Male	377	100	62.9	10.1	5.0	4.0	18.0
Female	323	100	67.7	9.6	2.8	5.0	14.9
Survey							
Male	226	100	62.1	8.4	3.5	6.2	19.8
Female	222	100	71.5	6.8	1.4	5.4	14.9
Agency							
Male	151	100	64.2	12.6	7.3	0.7	15.2
Female	101	100	59.4	15.8	5.9	4.0	14.9

$$\chi^2 = 4.2; \; df = 4; \; p > 0.05.$$

Table 32 is a presentation of attendance by color and source of information. Overall, whites have a higher rate of attendance than Negroes. These data conflict with previous studies which have shown the Negroes participate more than whites in such examinations.[5] Actually, the data indicate that Negroes and whites differ very little in refusals, valid excuses, and persons who were no longer in the sample. If the "not located" category is removed in the computation of attendance rates, the participation of Negroes and whites is about equal. An immediate conclusion from this finding is that greater effort must be expended in locating the non-white population.

TABLE 32

Response to Clinic Invitations by Race and Source of Sample Selection

Race and Source of Sample Selection	Response to Clinic Invitation			Reason for Nonattendance			
	No. of Persons	Total %	Attended	Not Located	No Longer in Sample	Excuse Offered	No Excuse Offered
Total							
White	548	100	67.6	7.8	4.2	4.9	15.5
Nonwhite	152	100	56.6	17.1	3.3	2.6	20.4
Survey							
White	355	100	68.8	5.9	2.8	6.2	16.3
Nonwhite	93	100	59.1	14.0	1.1	4.3	21.5
Agency							
White	193	100	65.3	11.4	6.7	2.6	14.0
Nonwhite	59	100	52.6	22.0	6.8	0.0	18.6

$$\chi^2 = 15.9; \; df = 4; \; p < 0.01$$

5. *Ibid.*

It was hypothesized that perhaps the time of appointment was related to attendance at the clinic. Since families tend to have a routine for their days, an unanticipated invitation, especially in the afternoon, might tend to lead to non-cooperation. The Chi-square test indicates that there is no statistically significant relationship between attendance rates and the time of appointment.

The factor of age proved to be a very important correlate of attendance as is seen in Table 33. Very young children had moderately low attendance, young school age children had the highest rates of attendance. It is possible that the use of the word "child" in the name of the study generated some resentment in the teenager and the young adult. Also, it is possible that these young adults had more positive control over their attendance than the younger children. Geographic mobility is to be noted in the fact that the older age category tended to be over-represented in the "no longer in sample" segment of the population. Furthermore, according to our data, there was a progressive tendency from age five to age twenty for persons to promise to appear at the scheduled time and then refuse to come at the last minute. This particular type of non-attendance is most disheartening because little can be done by way of insuring attendance once a promise of attendance has been given.

TABLE 33

Response to Clinic Invitations by Age

Age Years	Response to Clinic Invitation			Reason for Nonattendance			
	No. of Persons*	Total %	Attended	Not Located	No Longer in Sample	Excuse Offered	No Excuse Offered
0 to 4	87	100	58.7	12.6	4.6	8.0	16.1
5 to 9	195	100	81.6	9.2	1.5	2.6	5.1
10 to 14	213	100	71.8	6.1	1.9	3.8	16.4
15 to 21	198	100	47.0	12.1	8.6	4.5	27.8

$\chi^2 = 121.1$; df $= 9$; $p < 0.001$.

* There were seven cases for whom age was not known.

Table 34 presents the rates of attendance to the clinic in terms of the presumptive diagnosis of the child. Presumptive diagnosis means, in this case, the clinic into which the child was invited and does not indicate an absence of other conditions. These "primary diagnoses" were used to permit medical specialists to be brought in on certain days in addition to the pediatricians who staffed every clinic.

The data by diagnosis indicate that variation in attendance is related to presumptive diagnosis. The control subjects, the presumptively normal, had a low rate of attendance, as did the mentally retarded and emotionally disturbed. The highest rates were observed for patients reported to have chronic respiratory infections, those with orthopedic impairments, those with speech and hearing problems, and those with cleft palate or hare lip.

One may interpret these findings to mean that the highest attendance rates seem to be associated with conditions for which something can be done. Low attendance rates are associated with non-disabling conditions and conditions for which little, if anything, could realistically be done.

TABLE 34

Response to Clinic Invitations by Primary (or Presumptive) Diagnosis

Primary Presumptive Diagnosis	Response to Clinic Invitation			Reason for Nonattendance			
	No. of Persons	Total %	Attended	Not Located	No Longer in Sample	Excuse Offered	No Excuse Offered
Normal	163	100	63.2	10.4	0.0	9.2	17.2
Orthopedic	42	100	76.2	9.5	0.0	2.4	11.9
Epilepsy	23	100	60.9	0.0	0.0	17.4	21.7
Vision	88	100	60.2	12.5	3.4	3.4	20.5
Speech and hearing	90	100	75.6	10.0	0.0	1.1	13.3
Cleft palate	25	100	76.0	12.0	8.0	0.0	4.0
Mental retardation	62	100	54.8	8.1	14.5	3.2	19.4
Chronic respiratory	45	100	80.0	8.9	0.0	0.0	11.1
Heart	69	100	63.8	17.4	7.2	2.9	8.7
Orthodontic	24	100	70.8	4.2	0.0	8.3	16.7
Cerebral palsy	22	100	59.1	4.5	18.2	0.0	18.2
Skin	24	100	58.3	4.2	0.0	4.2	33.3
Emotional disturbance	23	100	39.2	4.3	21.7	0.0	34.8

A final analysis attempted concerned the relationship of attendance and the occupation of the head of the household. The Chi-square test did not show statistical significance, although a consistent direction of the findings was noted: a clear tendency existed for the attendance rates to drop in a linear fashion with the prestige value of the occupation of the head of the household due to an increase in non-locates and refusals.

Summary

In summary, the data on attendance rates from this clinic have been presented to stress one sort of "explanation" for non-attendance. These data suggest that a substantial proportion of non-attendance falls into the "not located" category. For these hard to locate groups, a more intensive search might be pursued with an earlier announcement of the time of clinic appointment. The real offender of the survey however is not the person who has a valid excuse (which averaged about five per cent overall), but the person who promises to come but never shows up, never calls, and never asks for a re-appointment. For some of these groups which consistently respond poorly (predominantly males, persons fifteen to twenty, and persons with no record of agency care), it is best to plan to use greater effort, or even to schedule additional clinic days. More intensive effort could also be used on persons with mild conditions such as skin defects or vision problems. In the case of persons with chronic and disabling conditions, perhaps another form of clinic, namely, the unassembled clinic or home examination, could be used with greater success. It is evident from this study that there is a diversity of reasons for non-attendance by different categories, and that no one procedure is adequate to cope with all situations. Future studies will probably have to adopt some procedure for working around the high non-attendance rates. This will probably take the form, as Cobb, King, and Chen suggest, of making a study of response rates part of the study design, directing added effort toward groups known to be poorly motivated, establishing alternate procedures where appropriate, and of adjusting the final results in accordance with the characteristics of known deviant groups.

CHAPTER IX

SOME FACTORS RELATING TO THE ADEQUACY OF MEDICAL CARE

As described in Chapter II, complete medical examinations were carried out on 456 presumptively normal and presumptively handicapped children drawn from those recorded in the agency records and the household survey. These examinations were designed to provide insight into the medical practices of Alamance County as well as to measure the degree of concordance between morbidity as measured by survey methods and by medical records. A staff conference was held following clinical examination where two decisions were made with respect to each child: first, consensus was reached with regard to the major conditions affecting the child and, second, recommendations were given for the care of each of the diagnoses. These recommendations form the basis of the major dependent variable used in this Chapter, namely whether or not the child was judged to be receiving *adequate* or *inadequate* medical care. The research question posed here is: what are the socio-personal and medical factors which are related to the handicapped child's receiving adequate medical care.

The Factors Studied

Several medical and socio-personal characteristics were hypothesized to have relevance to adequacy of care. They were (1) *family finances* which was thought to be relevant because our society uses a fee-for-service system of medical care; (2) *the existence or absence of medical services* in a county was thought to be relevant because health services generate interest as well as provide care; (3) the *social values of the community* were thought to be relevant: if a condition is not socially defined as a handicap it will not be treated because no care is sought and demand is not generated for that particular service.

Both medical and socio-personal factors were tested for their relevance to the receiving of adequate medical care. The medically relevant factors included diagnosis and severity of condition as judged by the examining physicians. The diagnoses studied were: orthopedic and neuromuscular conditions, epilepsy, vision defects, hearing disorders, cleft lip or palate, emotional disturbances, speech defects,

109

mental retardation, chronic respiratory conditions, heart disorders, orthodontic difficulties, cerebral palsy, chronic skin conditions, "other handicapping conditions," and normal children.* Severity of condition was judged as *none, mild, moderate,* or *severe* by the examining physicians.

The socio-personal factors studied included: age (in the following categories: 0-4, 5-9, 10-14, and 15-21); race (white and Negro); sex; family finances (judged as adequate, fair, or poor) ; working mother; and health agencies (the sources of medical assistance reported by the parents such as public welfare agencies, schools, hospitals, physicians in private practice and "other") .

Any or all of these factors may be related to the adequacy of the care afforded a handicapped child. The problem is one of evaluating the relative effects of these factors when they are considered as causally related to the adequacy of medical care. The simplest and most straightforward approach to this problem is a multiple regression analysis predicting to the adequacy of care. This test involves the use of a predictor set of variables mentioned earlier and the adequacy of medical care as a binary coded dependent variable.[1]

The regression analysis model permits the evaluation of the relative significance of each of the factors studied as well as the intercorrelations among the factors. For example, while age may be related to the receiving of medical care it may also be related to the diagnoses which a child is given. The model permits the removal of the effects of age, for example, and tests for loss in prediction when this factor is removed.

General Findings.

For the 456 children examined, there were 628 diagnoses of handicapping conditions and 109 completely normal children. This means that for the children with at least one handicap, there tended to be more than one condition affecting the child. For each diagnosis made at the clinic, the physicians judged whether or not the child was receiving adequate care. For 42 per cent of the conditions care was judged to be inadequate and recommendations for additional care were given.

---

* For a brief description of these categories, see Chapter I.
1. Stanley L. Warner, "Multivariate Regression of Dummy Variates Under Normality Assumptions," *Journal of the American Statistical Association* 586 (December, 1963) , pp. 1054-1063.

The regression model indicates that by using all of the socio-personal and medical factors indicated above, it is possible to predict statistically, the adequacy of care. The F ratio of 6.64 with 32 and 702 degrees of freedom is significant at the .001 level. Using all factors, the relative effects are:

Age: older children tend to be receiving less adequate medical care than younger children.

Race: Negroes receive less adequate medical care than whites.

Sex: females receive less adequate medical care than males.

Family finances: people judged as being poor receive the least adequate medical care.

Working mothers: children whose mothers were not working tended to receive less adequate medical care than those whose mothers were working.

Medical agencies: children served only by schools or by public welfare agencies tended to be receiving less adequate medical care.

Diagnoses: children handicapped with vision difficulties, hearing difficulties, emotional disorders, speech defects, mental retardation, chronic respiratory disorders, orthodontic disabilities, and cerebral palsy tended to be receiving the least adequate medical care.

Severity: children with moderate to severely disabling conditions receive less adequate medical care than those with mild conditions or those with no disability at all.

The task now becomes one of assessing individual contributions to the predictive system.

There is no significant loss to the predictive system when any of the following factors are removed singly: age, race, sex, working mother and the medical agencies from which the child is reported. These factors owe their predictive value to their intercorrelation with other factors in the system. The factors which are directly relevant and useful in making predictions are: the diagnostic categories, family finances and severity of the condition. Respectively, the variance ratios are 3.98 with 17 and 702 degrees of freedom; 8.23, with 22 and 702 degrees of freedom; and 27.07 with 3 and 702 degrees of freedom—all statistically significant at less than the .001 level. An analysis which is not included in this report indicated that, when severity of condition affecting the child is removed, all the diagnostic categories become much more highly related to the adequacy of care. This is merely a statistical expression of the fairly obvious fact that the less severely disabled the child and the more modest his needs the more likely he is to have received adequate care.

The independent removal of the effects may obscure the conjunctivity of effects. An attempt was made, therefore, to remove certain of these effects in combination. Three very important factors were family finances, diagnosis, and severity of condition. Taking these three factors out of the predictive set results in a significant loss of predictive ability; the F ratio of 8.23 with 22 and 702 degrees of freedom is significant at less than the .001 level. Furthermore, these three factors together account for 40.27 of the 42.61 sum of squares due to the total regression.

Independent Effects

The independent effects of individual factors were analyzed. We asked if, ignoring all other factors, it was possible to predict to the adequacy of care in terms of, say, age alone. In this analysis age by itself does predict to the adequacy of care. Older children tend to receive less adequate care than younger children; the F ratio is 3.80 with 3 and 731 degrees of freedom, which is significant at the .01 level. Race also predicts to the adequacy of care. Negroes receive less adequate care than whites; the F ratio equals 8.19 with 1 and 733 degrees of freedom which is significant at the .01 level. Sex does not predict significantly to adequacy of care. Family finances, however, did predict to adequacy of care, with poorer families receiving less adequate care than those with adequate or "fair" finances; the F ratio is 21.26 with 2 and 732 degrees of freedom. Neither the factor of working mother, nor the factor of the agency to which a child is referred predict significantly to the adequacy of care. Both severity of condition and a knowledge of the diagnoses, however, predict to the adequacy of medical care. The F ratio for severity is 27.07 with 3 and 731 degrees of freedom, which is significant at less than the .001 level. The F ratio for the diagnoses is 9.16 with 17 and 717 degrees of freedom which is also significant at less than the .001 level. For all conditions except epilepsy, classification as moderately or severely handicapping is related to receiving inadequate medical attention (as measured by the regression constants). This finding is apparently related to another interesting finding, namely that the majority of children with a significant handicap had *not* just one condition affecting them but several and were receiving care for only one of them.

Medical Effects

Since analyses to this point have shown that a significant proportion of the overall predictive system is related to diagnosis, and since services are created in relation to categories of medical diagnoses, it is important to consider the independent effects of specific diagnoses.

Presented in Table 35 are the independent effects of medical diagnosis and the variance ratio of their ability to predict adequacy of medical care. These data show that one can predict to the conditions being serviced and those not being serviced. Children diagnosed as emotionally disturbed, those having hearing defects, the educable and trainable mentally retarded, and the orthodontically defective received indaequate medical care. On the other hand, care was adequate if the child was disabled by orthopedic disability, epilepsy, cleft palate or a heart defect. Simply knowing that these conditions affected a child is sufficient information, on the average, to predict whether or not a child was receiving adequate medical attention as judged by examining physicians. For other conditions, namely vision, speech, chronic respiratory conditions, cerebral palsy,

TABLE 35

The Relationship Between Medical Diagnoses and the Possibility of Receiving Adequate Medical Care, Alamance County

Condition	F Ratio	Direction of Relationship	Care
Orthopedic conditions	9.26	+	Adequate
Epilepsy	4.10	+	Adequate
Vision defects	.41	+	NP
Hearing defects	7.43	—	Inadequate
Cleft palate	5.71	+	Adequate
Emotional disturbance	15.71	—	Inadequate
Speech disorders	2.07	—	NP
Mental retardation:			
Presumptive	.26	+	NP
Educable	24.78	—	Inadequate
Trainable	4.03	—	Inadequate
Custodial	.13	+	NP
Respiratory disorders	.16	—	NP
Heart conditions	7.65	+	Adequate
Orthodontic conditions	14.01	—	Inadequate
Cerebral palsy	.51	—	NP
Skin conditions	3.48	+	Adequate
Other	1.75	+	NP

$F_{1,733}$:   3.45 less than .05
        6.64 less than .01
        10.83 less than .001
NP = No Prediction

and skin conditions, the F ratio is not statistically significant and no predictions are possible.

The non-significance of the diagnostic categories of vision and speech defects, chronic respiratory conditions, cerebral palsy and skin conditions leads to questions concerning the interrelationship between adequacy of care and the socio-personal characteristics of the children and their families. Since the non-significant F ratio means that some are receiving care while others are not, the question becomes who is receiving care and who is not. If we cannot explain the non-reception of care in terms of the existence of medical and paramedical facilities, it is clear that factors other than facilities must be employed in explanation.

Socio-personal Characteristics and Medical Care

Thus far we have shown that medical and socio-personal factors affect the adequacy of medical care afforded the handicapped children of Alamance County, and that the removal of medical diagnoses, family finances, and the severity of the condition produces a statistically significant loss in predictive ability for the entire predictive system. Further, relating medical diagnoses alone to adequacy of care, three categories of medical conditions were found to exist: (1) conditions for which facilities are inadequate (mental retardation, emotional disturbance, hearing defects, and orthodontic defects); (2) conditions which are receiving adequate care (orthopedics, epilepsy, cleft palate, and heart defects); and (3) conditions which do not predict to adequacy of care (vision defects, speech defects, chronic respiratory conditions, cerebral palsy, skin conditions, and "other" defects). It seems appropriate to focus attention on the conditions in this latter category to see if the socio-personal characteristics of the children predict who are receiving aid and who are not.

For these conditions the total predictor set predicted adequacy of care. The F ratio was 2.64 with 11 and 241 degrees of freedom, which is significant at less than the .01 level. As was pointed out earlier, diagnosis alone did not predict to adequacy of care. Furthermore, there was no significant loss of prediction when any of the following was removed singly: age, race, and working mother. These factors, then, act together to predict adequacy of care and hence are interrelated to one another.

The next step was an evaluation of these socio-personal factors independently to determine the relation of each to the prediction of adequacy of care. Age was a significant predictor with older children receiving less adequate care than younger children. The F ratio was 2.64 with 3 and 249 degrees of freedom which is significant at less than the .05 level. In terms of race, Negro children were receiving less adequate medical care than white children. The F ratio was 4.69 with 1 and 251 degrees of freedom, which is significant at less than the .05 level. Poorer children received less adequate care than children with better finances. The F ratio was 4.00 with 2 and 250 degrees of freedom, which is significant at less than the .05 level. Severity of condition also predicted to the adequacy of care, with the least disabled children receiving the most adequate care. The F ratio was 3.72 with 3 and 249 degrees of freedom, which is significant at less than the .05 level. Neither working mother nor sex had independent significance in predicting to the adequacy of medical care.

In short, given the availability of medical facilities and considering only those conditions for which the diagnosis did not predict to the adequacy of care, the key factors in determining whether or not a child was receiving care were *age, race, family finances* and *severity of conditions.* Typically, for this group of conditions, being Negro, poor, older and having a more severe condition predicted to receiving less adequate care. Being white, of a family with more adequate finances, younger and having a less severe condition predicted to more adequate care.

Discussion

There are several ways of estimating the adequacy of medical facilities and personnel. One of the most common is in terms of ratio to population: e.g., hospital beds per 1,000, physicians per 10,000. This has obvious disadvantages because standards based on such ratios are arbitrary and do not take into account either the difference between ideal needs and effective demand or the effect which increasing the availability of services may have in enhancing perceived need and demand. In other words, they take no account of the various factors other than availability which enter into the determination of whether needed services are actually obtained.

Perhaps the ideal approach to the question would be an intensive investigation of a representative sample of handicapped children in an effort to determine for each case those needs which have and those which have not been adequately met and to evaluate all the factors contributing to failure to receive adequate care. Such an investigation was outside the possibilities of the present study.

The problem, therefore, was approached by two less direct analyses. In Chapter V interagency referral patterns were analyzed and the part which deficiencies and inconsistencies of the referral mechanism played in the failure of handicapped children to receive all the services they need was explored. By implication, some needed services and facilities were found to be unavailable.

In the present chapter an analysis is made for the 456 children given examinations in the clinic of a number of factors associated with receiving or failing to receive care determined by the examining team to be needed. There were found to be three groups of conditions, those for which care had been inadequate regardless of socio-personal factors, those for which it had been generally adequate, and those for which it had been adequate for some children, but inadequate for others. With respect to the first group, mental retardation, emotional disturbance, hearing defects and orthodontic defects, it can be reasonably deduced that needed services and facilities were unavailable or at least grossly inadequate.

For the second group, orthopedic conditions, epilepsy, cleft palate and heart defects, needed care had generally been received, so the presumption is that services and facilities were adequate so far as diagnosis and treatment for the specific conditions are concerned. This does not, of course, say that the needs of the "whole child" with these conditions were necessarily met. This aspect of the problem is discussed in the final chapter.

For the third group of conditions, vision defects, speech defects, chronic respiratory conditions, cerebral palsy, and skin conditions, various socio-personal characteristics were found to influence whether or not needed care was received. It would appear that there are available services and facilities for these conditions, but being older, being poor, being a Negro, or having a more severe condition unfavorably influences the receiving of adequate care. The two factors of economic circumstance and race are, of course, closely related, and this association with inadequate care suggests that the costs of care present a barrier. Other factors not included in our analysis, however, are probably also significant: definition of handicapping condition, the way in which agencies through which care might be secured are perceived, ignorance of services which may be available, etc. Thus, there are social and educational as well as medical components to the problem presented by these conditions.

There is reason to doubt that available facilities and services for these conditions would be adequate if barriers of cost and attitude were overcome. The provision of needed services for the handicapped children of the county, therefore, must include enhancement of the adequacy and availability of specific services both for these conditions and for those in the first group where services were more obviously lacking: mental retardation, emotional disturbance, hearing defects and orthodontic defects. Looking at these conditions individually we note that two, skin conditions and chronic respiratory conditions, have traditionally not been the objects of special community programs or facilities. An exception among chronic respiratory conditions is tuberculosis, but this was not involved in the children diagnosed as having respiratory problems. Whether or not special facilities should be provided is a question which can be answered only by a more detailed study of the specific problems, but certainly there is need for education and for more adequate financial provision for care of the medically indigent with diseases in these categories.

For the other three conditions, vision and speech defects and cerebral palsy there are community programs. The fact that the children from families with more adequate finances generally receive care would suggest that the community programs are inadequate and that those who can afford to do so get part or all of their needed care privately. There appear to be, therefore, three aspects of community programs for these conditions which need attention:

1. The services and facilities themselves need reevaluation as a prelude to substantial strengthening and expansion.

2. There needs to be more adequate financial provision for services to those children whose parents are indigent or at least unable to pay for care which is needed.

3. A strong educational effort is needed to enhance understanding, motivation and more effective use of available resources on the part of parents. This should include measures especially designed to reach the population groups which have the poorest understanding and receive the poorest care: the lower social classes, and particularly Negroes.

CHAPTER X

SUMMARY, RECOMMENDATIONS AND SUGGESTIONS FOR FURTHER RESEARCH

This chapter summarizes the major findings of the study in terms of the five objectives set forth in the first chapter, and discusses the implications of the findings in terms of future planning and extension of services for handicapped children. Following this discussion suggestions are presented for further research in the field of handicapping conditions among children.

Prevalence Rates

The prevalence rates revealed by the clinical examinations proved to be much higher than expected and much higher than previous studies and estimates had indicated. When these conditions were classified by severity of disability, it was revealed that 65 per cent of conditions caused no disability or only minimal disability. The prevalence rates of conditions causing moderate or severe disability were more nearly in line with estimates from other sources, and these are the rates we feel most relevant to the need and planning for facilities and services.

The needs which this high prevalence indicates are tremendous, and the problem is magnified by the fact that a large proportion of the existing conditions go unrecognized. Assuming that the prevalence rates derived from agency records represent the recognized handicapping conditions, the total number of significant handicapping conditions actually present in the community is more than twice the number which have been recognized.

This "recognition rate" is not, of course, the same for all handicapping conditions. The agency and clinical examination rates for orthopedic and heart conditions were rather comparable, indicating that children with these conditions have generally been recognized. On the other hand, only six per cent of orthodontic conditions and seventeen per cent of the cases with epilepsy had been recorded. Other conditions were intermediate, with from 18 to 52 per cent of the cases recognized. One striking finding was the large number of children with a record of one handicapping condition who had one or more additional conditions which were not previously recorded. Some of this omission of recording was doubtless due to the "inclusive" definitions used, but the larger part appeared to be related to a lack of recognition.

It is evident from the foregoing discussion that a major problem to be solved is that of case finding. Efforts need to be directed particularly at devising ways with which to find those children suffering from conditions with low recognition rates: orthodontic defects, epilepsy, chronic skin conditions, hearing defects, chronic respiratory conditions and, perhaps, cerebral palsy, although the lack of recognition of this condition is probably more apparent than real, because it is related to the inadequacy of community services available to these children.

Extent of Disability

The extent of disability was approached in two ways as described in Chapter II. Twenty per cent of the children of the county were estimated to have conditions classified as moderate to severe. In Table 7 disability of the agency and survey children examined in the clinic is estimated in terms of vocational limitation. Twenty-two per cent of survey examinees and 43 per cent of agency examinees had some vocational limitation and three and five per cent, respectively, were totally restricted.

Because the study was medically oriented rather than casework oriented, we were not especially successful in gaining insight into factors other than the medical conditions themselves which contributed to disability except in those instances where children with severely disabling or disfiguring conditions had secondary emotional problems. In part, such emotional disturbance was directly secondary to the physical disability and in part it derived from family problems created or aggravated by having a severely disabled child in the home.

Quite clearly, however, disability is related to social definitions. For the agency data, for example, diagnoses and disability were apparently related to sex, race and financial status of the family. As has been shown, what is a serious problem in one social status category is not a problem at all in another. Orthodontic problems were rarely recognized in Negro females.

Methods of Estimating Prevalence

Three methods of estimating prevalence rates of handicapping conditions were used. As discussed previously, the first, a study of records of health agents and agencies, seriously underestimated prevalence rates, and the degrees of underestimation for different conditions varied widely. It is perhaps no occasion for surprise that health records provided a poor picture of the needs of the county's children. For one thing, they are based in the main on children for whom help has been sought. For another, they are limited by the objectives, responsibilities and resources of the organizations which maintain them, by the informal procedures and relationships which help determine how agencies really work, and by the interests and value judgments of individual workers responsible for record creation and maintenance.

There is no short cut to estimating prevalence rates through using a single agency as a "best source." Only the summation of records from all sources can serve adequately to define the prevalence of handicapping conditions as known to health agencies.

In spite of its shortcomings in providing estimations of prevalence, at least three considerations might commend a records survey to communities interested in gaining insight into their children's handicapping problems. First, it is a feasible procedure for a local community. Second, it gives a picture of the handicapping conditions which have been recognized and for which help has been sought. In this way it serves to highlight the specialization of programs and services which inevitably occurs. Furthermore, comparison of the rates thus derived with more adequate estimates, such as those based on our clinical examinations, provides an indication of the degree of adequacy of health agents and programs. Third, and perhaps most important, such a survey can provide to the community and to the agencies themselves, valuable insights into both formal and informal procedures and relationships within and between agencies and into actual practices and emphases as these relate to professed purposes, programs and goals, pointing up gaps and weaknesses.

The household survey phase of the study was designed to measure parental recognition of and concern about possibly handicapping conditions among their children. It is obvious that much more than the existence of a verifiable condition was portrayed by positive answers to the questionnaire, yet the remarkable thing is that it was possible to verify the existence of some condition in 75 per cent of the sample of children examined in the clinic.

Most health surveys have chosen to limit their prevalence estimates by using screening questions, questions which exclude those with no or only mild disability. Such a procedure assumes that the survey method is one where such screening can be used. No such assumption was made here. Included were all disabilities, with exclusions based on medical judgment.

As might be expected, the survey overestimated the prevalence of handicapping conditions, particularly those conditions like skin and respiratory diseases which are especially obvious to parents. The surveys in Alamance and Halifax Counties showed inconsistencies in rates which appeared to be due more to socio-cultural differences than to real differences of prevalence. Correction factors certainly have to be applied to data secured in this way and, unfortunately, it is doubtful that correction factors, such as those derived in Alamance County from the clinical examinations, will be generalizable to counties with different socio-cultural characteristics. The survey method employed here could be used to determine the utility of screening questions by defining the differentials in parental concern in terms of socio-cultural variables.

The household survey proved to be a feasible undertaking which was relatively inexpensive. Similar surveys should be within the capabilities of most communities to carry out, provided competent consultation is secured and care is exercised in enlisting and training the volunteer interviewers. In spite of its limitations in providing adequate and unbiased prevalence estimates, it can make two distinct contributions. First, it can provide a crude index of the order of magnitude of problems of childhood handicapping, and, second, it can serve to inform and involve community leaders in the problems as a prelude to efforts to develop more adequate services and facilities for children afflicted with these conditions.

The final study of morbidity was the clinical examinations. Based upon careful and comprehensive examinations, together with a group judgment by all who participated in the examinations, a diagnosis, or diagnoses, and an estimate of disability were determined for each of the 456 children examined. Forty-three per cent of the group had some recordable condition, only seven percentage points lower than the 50 per cent reported by parents. This is really a surprisingly large proportion estimated to be handicapped. Of course, when classified by severity, the majority of these conditions did not fall into the moderate or severe categories which have been suggested as providing a more realistic basis for evaluating facility and service needs. Even these adjusted rates are, however, unexpectedly high. The greatest problems, in terms of numbers of children affected, are in the field of mental health, mental retardation and emotional disturbance. Next come orthodontic conditions, chronic respiratory conditions and defects of vision. Cleft palate and cerebral palsy do not involve so many children, but the magnitude of the problems they present to the child and his parents calls for a high level of community concern and action.

Factors Related to Adequacy of Care

These three phases of the study were not just steps to determine morbidity rates. Of equal or greater significance, they were opportunities to gain insight into many of the practices, assumptions and attitudes involved in the important area of medical care related to children with special needs. These factors have profound implications in efforts to meet the needs of these children. For example, the analyses in Chapter IX revealed that many factors other than availability of services were important in determining whether handicapped children received the care they needed. Social class, economic status, education, age, race, even sex were among the significant determinants of receiving adequate care.

Moreover, it was evident throughout the study that many factors not so susceptible of neat analysis played important roles in determining whether children with handicapping conditions received needed care for which services were actually available. Among these are the social folkways and values of the community, the organization, goals, special interests and interrelationships of community agencies and legal and policy restrictions on services and programs. These factors are as important as the availability of services and facilities in determining whether handicapped children really receive the care they need, and they must receive important consideration in any community planning for expansion and improvement of services in this area.

Service and Facility Needs

The evaluation of service needs was approached by an analysis of the extent to which the children examined in the clinic had received the care which the examining team agreed was needed. We feel that this analysis can be of more practical value than one employing, for instance, arbitrary ratios of personnel and facilities to population.

When needed care had not been received, we sought to determine why. The answer to the question of why care had not been received was admittedly often a matter of judgment, based as it was on information obtained at the time of examination and on the knowledge of community resources, facilities and practices acquired in other phases of the study.

There were a number of specific inadequacies and needs, many of which are implicit in the results of the analysis in the previous chapter of conditions for which inadequate care was received. These specific needs will be listed and discussed briefly.

1. *Services for Children with Speech Defects*—The only speech therapy available locally was that provided by two speech therapists in the schools. Positions were set up for a total of six therapists, but qualified people to fill them were not available. This points up an important aspect of the problem which the local community cannot solve, the need for greatly expanded facilities for training speech therapists.

However, even if all available positions had been filled, they would have been inadequate to meet the needs of the school children with speech problems. Moreover, there were no local facilities for speech therapy for pre-school children, nor for those children with more severe problems requiring highly skilled diagnostic and treatment measures. Such facilities are available at nearby medical centers, but they would be quickly overwhelmed if all eligible children were to seek care.

2. *A Hearing Program*—There was no effective program for identifying children with hearing problems. There needs to be a comprehensive program of periodic audiometric testing of school children and referral for appropriate otologic examination and care of all children found with significant loss of hearing acuity.

Education of the public is also needed regarding the importance of ear infections and the need to have a thorough examination of ears which continue to discharge more than a week or two. Public agencies should be prepared to provide or finance medical referral for those not able to secure care from private physicians.

3. *A Program of Eye Examinations*—There was an extensive program of vision screening in school children, using the Snellen tests, but follow-up of those found to have defective vision was inadequate. There is need for more systematic referral for ophthalmologic examination, reinforced by an educational program and supplemented by clinics at which those unable to secure private care may be examined by an ophthalmologist.

4. *A Greatly Expanded Program in Mental Health*—By far the largest groups of handicapped children are the mentally retarded and the emotionally disturbed. Although it did not realize their magnitude, the community was concerned about these problems, especially mental retardation, and was seeking to expand its efforts in this field.

The number of classes for the retarded has been increasing each year, and, as the study was being concluded, plans had been completed for a local mental health clinic. These developments should make a substantial impact on the following specific needs:

More adequate psychological testing services for children

A larger number of teachers and classes for the mentally retarded

Expanded facilities for the trainable mentally retarded, including facilities for Negro children

A center to provide diagnosis and outpatient treatment for emotionally disturbed children.

Psychiatric social services for the parents of children with serious mental and emotional problems.

5. *Services for those with Cerebral Palsy*—There need to be additional special classes for cerebral palsy children. Particularly needed is a day care facility including among its services physical, occupational, recreational and speech therapy and training in the activities of daily living.

6. *Seizure Program*—Although a majority of the children examined who were found to have seizures were under medical supervision and had reasonably good control, there was no local facility to which difficult diagnostic or treatment problems could be referred. Such specialized services were available in nearby medical centers, but could care for only a limited number of children. There is, therefore, need for a seizure clinic, either locally or nearby, to which the physicians and health agencies can refer all the children presenting special problems and through which enhanced understanding of seizure problems can be promoted among parents, patients and public.

7. *Orthodontic Services*—As has been pointed out, except for the more extreme degrees, orthodontic deformities were not generally considered to be handicapping. This may be partly associated with the fact that orthodontic services were unavailable locally. In any event, public support or care needs to be provided for those children from low income families who have marked deformities. The con-

siderable costs of such a program are not the only obstacle to its implementation. There are just not enough orthodontists available and the supply is likely to increase very slowly.

Perhaps a more attainable immediate objective would be development of a pre-school dental program comparable to the school dental program already in operation, and intensification of efforts to educate parents to the importance of care of the baby teeth as a measure to prevent orthodontic deformity of the permanent teeth. Another important preventive measure would be fluoridation of the public water supplies of the county.

8. *Special Problems of those with Severe Multiple Handicaps*—The children with severe multiple handicaps are not a large proportion of the total number of handicapped, but their problems are so overwhelming to the children, their parents and the community that they deserve urgent consideration. These are children, for example, who are both blind and deaf, or blind or deaf and mentally retarded, who need institutional care for both of their handicaps. Unfortunately, although excellent state institutions exist for care of children with *one* of these conditions, they do not have personnel or facilities to meet the needs of those with a second serious limitation. Here is a need which deserves serious attention from those concerned with the state's unfortunate children.

In the enumeration of these problems in specific areas, brief reference has been made to three general needs which really apply to all handicapping categories. The first, as might be expected, is for free or part pay clinics and/or financial assistance for services needed by children which their parents cannot provide for reasons of medical indigency or the fact that the services are so expensive. Some assistance is, of course, available, but it is inadequate to the need. Provisions for financial assistance should be designed to encourage parents to secure services through physicians of their own choice to the extent possible, but should have policies flexible enough not to constitute a deterrent to securing care. This area offers a splendid opportunity for cooperative planning between the medical and dental professions and the agencies of the community.

The second need is for medical social and counselling services. The child with a serious handicapping condition presents severe problems to his parents and family beyond the need for suitable medical and related care. Just providing physical care is often an overwhelming burden. The strain on interfamily relationships and the emotional problems generated among siblings may be quite severe. In contacts with parents in the clinic the need was demonstrated again and again for counselling and support and for guidance in making the most effective use of available resources. Public health nurses can, perhaps, provide this service if they are given the responsibility and sufficient time in their schedules. However, it may be more effective and logical to employ medical social workers for this purpose. The assignment of one or more medical social workers with specific responsibility for handicapped children to either the Health or Welfare Department would make available a much needed dimension to the community's efforts in behalf of handicapped children.

A third need is for a broadly based, soundly conceived, energetically pursued community educational program. Fear, prejudice, ignorance of available sources of help and care, an "image" of community agencies which is inadequate or distorted, and a lack of motivation play an important part in the failure of many children to receive care even though facilities are actually available. In many ways, attacking these problems is a larger challenge than the development of needed services and facilities, but it is a challenge which must be met if handicapped children are to receive the care they need.

The feature of services to the handicapped which impressed us most forcibly was their specialization and fragmentation, the lack of systematic, continuous communication and referral between health agents and agencies, and the fact that there was no agency which was in a position to provide a measure of coordination among the diverse agencies and services which are involved. There are many excellent programs and services, but in practice they seem to follow the biblical injunction, "Let not thy right hand know what thy left hand doeth." Services are generally provided for specific conditions, e.g., orthopedic conditions, speech problems, rheumatic heart disease, etc. As a result, a child may receive excellent care for a specific condition for which he seeks attention, but fail to have note taken of coexisting conditions or to have any overall consideration of his needs as a child.

This situation is by no means unique to Alamance County, but probably exists in every community in the country to greater or lesser degree. It is, indeed, implicit in the dispersal of responsibility for various aspects of health care and services among many individuals and agencies and the specialization of both physicians and programs. Combined with the detrimental influence of such factors as social attitudes, the legal and policy limitations and special interests of voluntary and official programs, specialization results in inefficient use of existing services and facilities and deprives many children of needed services which are actually available.

It should be made clear that as far as Alamance County is concerned, this inadequate communication was not due to any lack of cordiality or cooperativeness among the various agencies or between the agencies and community practitioners. A friendly and cooperative feeling was quite evident and there was a great deal more informal interchange than appeared in the records. It was simply that there was no mechanism or plan for systematic referral and exchange of information and no individual or agency which could assume concern for the whole child.

It is our considered judgment that the greatest need in the whole field of childhood handicapping is for a program which can provide for the coordination of all the interests and services in the community, facilitate the needed communication and referral, and assure that the focus of service will be the child and his total needs and not just a specific handicapping condition.

Recommendations

It is beyond the scope of a study such as this to provide a detailed blue print for solving all the problems it has uncovered. In a very real sense the enumeration of shortcomings and needs for programs and services carries its own recommendation: community effort to meet these deficiencies. Unfortunately, it is not quite so simple, and it is deemed appropriate to suggest some general approaches which might offer hope of progress toward solving some of the more serious problems and to point to a few specific measures we feel should be considered. These are based on Alamance County, but are offered in the hope that they may, in principle at least, have much wider application.

It is evident that not all needs are equally urgent; nor can all be met in "one fell swoop." The determination of priorities, of the format of services to be developed and their relationship to existing agencies and programs is a problem which calls for intensive, coordinated community planning. A logical approach to such planning is a community Council for Handicapped Children, or perhaps a better name would be, Council for Children with Special Needs. Such a council should broadly represent both official and voluntary agencies, the medical and dental professions and the public, and should have official recognition if not official status. It should have explicit responsibility for establishing mechanisms of coordination and communication, for maintaining a central file of handicapped children, for continually evaluating service needs and effectiveness and for stimulating policies and programs to make the child and his total needs, rather than a diagnostic entity, the focus of concern.

To meet effectively such responsiblities the Council will have to have available to it full-time staff and adequate financial support from official and/or voluntary sources. Just how it is set up, its place in the organizational structure of the community and how it is financed are matters to be determined by the community. Since part of the problem is that there are already so many agencies concerned with handicapped children, rather than creating a new agency, it may be better to have the Council function through an existing agency, assigning the full-time staff to it, to carry out responsibilities related to handicapped children within the framework of policies developed by the Council. There is logic for considering the Health Department in this regard.

Much has been said throughout this report of the problem of the whole child and of the fact that available services tend to be oriented to specific handicapping conditions rather than to a child who, in addition to the needs of all children, has special needs growing out of one or more handicapping conditions. It is, perhaps, inevitable that services and facilities be designed to meet particular categorical needs. What is necessary, then, if the needs of the child as a child are to have proper attention is, first, a strong and continuing emphasis on the philosophy of the "whole child" on the part of every agency involved with children's health needs, and, second, specific measures by which this concept can find practical expression.

One such measure is the incorporation in every program for the care of handicapped children, by whomever provided, of a policy that every child with a significant or potentially significant condition shall have a complete pediatric history and examination and psychological tests. Another is the establishment of a clinic at which such examinations and tests can be done on children unable to secure them privately, giving special attention to children too old for "well baby" clinics and too young for school. The North Carolina State Board of Health is promoting and giving support to the establishment of clinics for initial examination and periodic observation of children with special problems, and these give promise of meeting, in part at least, this need. The Council on Children with Special Needs and the central file of handicapped children suggested above will help foster the "holistic" approach.

State programs and agencies were not specifically surveyed in this study, although insight was gained into some of the needs and deficiencies as these related to the children of Alamance County. Certainly, since many specific services are provided by state agencies or institutions, and others are provided under state policies or are supervised by state agencies, a number of the deficiencies which have been described have direct statewide implications. Some services, such as referral centers for the special problems in speech, hearing, seizures and mental illness cannot be provided in each local community, but there must be centers where these services are available, adequate in scope and quality, and conveniently located. This requires planning and promotion from the state level. Recruitment and training programs for professional personnel require consideration on a statewide or even regional basis.

In the light of these problems and of the number and variety of state agencies and institutions which have direct involvement in services for handicapped children, it is clear that there needs to be at the state level some similar mechanism or council for coordinated planning and program development which has been demonstrated at the county level. It is our opinion that such a body should have at least quasi-official status through legislative authorization. Its basic support should be from state funds. All official agencies and institutions and all voluntary agencies which promote or support programs in the field should be represented, and there should be at least some full-time staff, either directly under the Council or through one of the participating agencies.

Suggestions for Further Research

A study such as this answers some questions. It raises many others which can be answered only by further research. From the many interesting possibilities for further research which have suggested themselves in the course of the study we have selected those which follow as having particular significance to understanding the problems involved in discovering those children with handicapping conditions and meeting effectively their total needs.

1. *Study in depth of a selected sample of children with handicapping conditions, using the case history approach*—Such a study would have several objectives. First would be a determination of the image of various health agencies as perceived by people in different economic and socio-cultural groups and the way these relate to seek-

ing or not seeking aid. Aspects of this image which are detrimental to seeking and receiving needed care should be evaluated to determine whether they represent practices or policies which need reconsideration and possible change by the agencies or erroneous conceptions on the part of certain population groups which call for corrective educational efforts.

Closely related to this is a determination of the processes by means of which children have received care as described by parents. This should bring into focus the specific areas where lack of understanding, failures of coordination and legal and policy limitations serve to limit the securing of needed care, as well as those needed services and facilities which are simply not available.

2. *Study of informal channels of communication*—People learn about many of the sources of assistance which they use through various channels other than those specifically designed for and depended upon for dissemination of this information. How these informal channels relate to the formal channels, the extent to which they help or hinder seeking and receiving appropriate care, and how they may be utilized more effectively are insights which can be quite significant in the accomplishment of the desired goals in meeting the needs of handicapped children. Closely related to such a study might be the investigation of channels of communication and referral known to and utilized by people in the health professions. It may be that lack of awareness on the part of physicians, for example, of all the sources of assistance is an important limiting factor in giving appropriate referrals.

3. *Study of the differential goals and expectations of different groups in the community*—What do the practicing physicians see as goals in the care of the handicapped and as their role in this care? What do they expect of the community agencies? What responsibilities do they perceive themselves as having to the community agencies and their programs? What do health workers, welfare workers and teachers see as goals in the care of the handicapped and as their role in this care? What do they expect of the practicing physicians? There is reason to wonder whether some of the inadequacies and confusion in the provision of care may not be due to differences in perceived goals and expectations among these groups. The relationship of the goals and expectations of these groups to those of various segments of the population are also highly pertinent to the provision of care.

4. *Study of the relationship of definable elements of community structure and socio-cultural pattern to health awareness*—There was a strong suggestion that differences in educational level and other socio-cultural factors in Alamance and Halifax Counties were associated with differences in health awareness and that these differences in health awareness accounted, at least in part, for the lower prevalence rates elicited in the Halifax household survey. Conceivably other elements of the community structure such as geographic unity or diversity, orientation of the power structure, etc., may also affect health awareness. As imperfect an instrument as the questionnaire used in the household surveys is, its use in additional counties, supplemented by accurate description of the factors whose relationship is to be measured, should provide insights into these relationships. Such replication will also afford an opportunity for badly needed further study of response bias.

5. *Establishment of a means of coordination, such as the suggested Community Council for Children with Special Needs offers research opportunities*—A study of the experience of developing such a council, the methods used and the problems encountered, would provide valuable insight into the way communities work. Its effectiveness and limitations in bringing about coordination would need to be evaluated. Such a council would present the opportunity to experiment with and evaluate various approaches to health education of the elements in the community which are difficult to reach.

6. *A continuing clinic, operating for a period each year, to examine a sample of county children, both handicapped and presumably normal*—Provision for the annual examination and evaluation of a sample of county children, similar to the clinical examinations which were a part of this study, would provide tremendous opportunities to measure changes and progress relating to the recognition and care of handicapping conditions. It would provide a means of evaluating the effectiveness of efforts to bring about coordination and to foster the concept of the whole child, and would keep in the focus of community attention the areas of unmet need.

Such a clinic would be a rather large undertaking for most communities, and probably would require outside grant support and the cooperation of specialists and agencies outside the county. It must, however, be community-based, have part of its financial support from local sources, and be developed with the enthusiastic participation of the local medical and dental professions and community agencies.

There are available sources from which it should be possible to secure the needed outside financial support.

In conclusion, it is the hope of the authors not only that the information secured in this study will be of assistance to others who are concerned with the needs of handicapped children, but also that others will be stimulated to seek the answers to some of the significant questions the study has raised but failed to answer. It is especially hoped that the citizens and agencies of Alamance and Halifax Counties may build on the interest which has been created and the insights which have been achieved to develop expanded programs for meeting the needs of handicapped children, and to carry forward some of the further studies which have been suggested by this research.

APPENDIX

MAJOR FORMS USED IN THE SURVEY

HANDICAPPED CHILDREN SURVEY: FORM III

Register _____   _____

Date of last entry _____   _____

Primary Diagnosis_____ Date _____   _____

Diagnosis_____   _____

Diagnosis _____   _____

Total_____   _____

By_____   _____

Date _____   _____

Source of referral_____   _____

Date first known_____   _____

Care_____   _____

Name_____Initials_____

Date of birth_____Sex_____Race_____

Disposition_____

Income_____Siblings_____

Occupation_____

Other agencies_____

         _____

         _____

(For summarizing information in registers)

CONFIDENTIAL

I.D. No. _____

CHILD HEALTH SURVEY: ALAMANCE COUNTY

Name of Respondent

Head of Household

Address or description
of location of house

| Telephone No. | Best time to call |

INTERVIEW RECORD

Record date, time of call and interviewing time	Date and time of call				
	1	2	3	4	5
DATE					
Interview Time Start					
End					

Reason for non-interview_____

_____

_____

Interviewer_____   Date _____

EDITING RECORD

Edited by_____Date_____Passed_____

Comments_____Failed_____

1. Are there any other living quarters, occupied or
   vacant in this building (apartment)?   No   Yes

2. Is there any other building on this property for
   people to live in, either occupied or vacant?   No   Yes

3. Does anyone else living in this building use YOUR
   ENTRANCE to get to his living quarters?   No   Yes

INSTRUCTIONS: If "yes" to questions 1, 2, or 3, determine the location or address of the
              dwelling unit or units, record the location or address on the face of sheet
              of additional questionnaire IMMEDIATELY so that you will not forget to
              interview at those dwellings.

4. Now I would like to make a list of all the people living in this household.
   (a) What is the name of the head of this household? (enter name in first line below)
   (b) What are the names of all other persons who live here? (list below)
   (c) Do any (other) lodgers or roomers live here? (IF YES: list below)
   (d) Is there anyone else who lives here who is now away on business? On a visit? In a hospital, or other institution? (IF YES: list below)

INSTRUCTIONS: Health portion of questionnaire must be completed for all persons 20 years old or less. Circle the number by all persons 20 or less so that you will not forget to ask the health questionnaire for them. When the health questionnaire is completed for that person, blacken in the circle around the number.

Last name	First & Initial	5. How is ... related to the head of household (enter in detail, e.g. wife, son, step-son, partner, Lodger, etc.)	6. Race (circle)	7. Sex (circle)	8. How old was ... on their last birthday	9. What was ... date of birth (enter month, day and year)	10. What is highest grade in school .... completed? (give last year as: 1, 3 or 19)	11. If 14+ is ... Married Widowed Divorced or Separated Never Married
1.		HEAD	W Ne O	M F				M WI / DS NM
2.			W Ne O	M F				M WI / DS NM
3.			W Ne O	M F				M WI / DS NM
4.			W Ne O	M F				M WI / DS NM
5.			W Ne O	M F				M WI / DS NM
6.			W Ne O	M F				M WI / DS NM
7.			W Ne O	M F .				M WI / DS NM
8.			W Ne O	M F				M WI / DS NM
9.			W Ne O	M F				M WI / DS NM
10.			W Ne O	M F				M WI / DS NM

12. How long has this family lived in this country? _____ Mos. _____ Yrs.

13. What kind of work does head of house usually do for a living? (describe in detail)

14. In what business or industry is this work usually done? (describe in detail)

15. What is the name of your family doctor, or the last doctor you saw?
Dr. _____
Address _____

To the interviewer: What is your estimate of this family's social standing in THEIR community?
1. Upper class   2. Middle   3. Working   4. Lower
What kind of condition is their house of dwelling in?
Excellent _____   Good _____   Fair _____   Poor _____

139

C O N F I D E N T I A L

I. D. No._____

CHILD HEALTH SURVEY: ALAMANCE COUNTY

PART II

Name of Respondent:

Name of Youth   Number:

1. Does .... have cerebral palsy, multiple sclerosis, musclar
   dystrophy or other similar condition?   _____No _____Yes

2. Has .... ever had any paralysis of any kind, or had poor use
   of his legs, arms, feet, hands or fingers?   _____No _____Yes

3. Has .... ever had any repeated trouble with his back or spine,
   or any permanent stiffness or deformity of the foot, leg, arm,
   fingers or back?   _____No _____Yes

4. Is .... missing any fingers, hand or arm, toes, foot or leg,
   or does he have a club foot or deformed hand, regardless of
   the amount of correction or care?   _____No _____Yes

5. Has .... ever had any trouble with his balance or coordination
   or does he ever have any jerking or twitching in his arms, legs,
   hands, face or other part of the body?   _____No _____Yes

   a. If answer is "Yes" to Questions 1, 2, 3, 4, or 5, ask:
       What are .... symptoms? (Circle above and detail)

       _____

       _____

       _____

   b. Has .... ever been to a physician for this difficulty?   _____No _____Yes

                  ----

6. Has .... ever been known to suffer from epilepsy, (no matter
   how well it is now treated or controlled)?   _____No _____Yes

7. Has .... had more than one convulsion, fit, or spell in his
   life?   _____No _____Yes

8. Has .... had any convulsions, fits or spells after he was
   three years old?   _____No _____Yes

                  ----

9. Has .... ever had frequent crossing, rolling or twitching of the eyeball (not the eyelid)?   _____No   _____Yes

10. Has .... ever had serious trouble seeing without glasses?   _____No   _____Yes

11. Has .... ever had serious trouble seeing even when wearing glasses?   _____No   _____Yes

If answer is "Yes" to 9, 10, or 11, ask:
Would you describe .... problem?

_____

_____

_____

----

12. Is .... hard of hearing or is he suspected of having hearing trouble?   _____No   _____Yes

13. Does .... suffer from deafness or serious trouble with hearing or does he presently use an aid to hearing?   _____No   _____Yes

----

14. Does :... have a harelip or cleft palate, regardless of the amount of correction or care?   _____No   _____Yes

----

15. Does .... ever have violent temper outbursts which he is not able to control or does he ever have spells when he stares straight ahead, drops things or falls down without reason?   _____No   _____Yes

16. Does .... ever act peculiarly or not quite right, or does he often have a lot of difficulty in getting along with other children (or people)?   _____No   _____Yes

17. Has anyone like the doctor, school teacher, minister or some other responsible person ever felt that .... has personality trouble or trouble getting along with people?   _____No   _____Yes

----

18. Has .... ever had any speech defect or serious trouble speaking (even though it might have been corrected)?   _____No   _____Yes

19. Does .... lisp, use baby talk or talk in any way that is not right for his age?   _____No   _____Yes

If answer is "Yes" to 18 or 19 ask: Would you describe his speech:

_____

_____

_____

141

20. Was .... unusually late in:

    a. learning to sit up?   _____No _____Yes

       If answer is "Yes," do you know why?_____

       _____

    b. beginning to walk?   _____No _____Yes

       If answer is "Yes," do you know why?_____

       _____

21. Is .... seriously behind other children his age in any way?   _____No _____Yes

    If answer is "Yes," in what ways and why?_____ .

    _____

    _____

22. Is .... mentally retarded or slow witted, or does he have
serious difficulty in learning or remembering things?   _____No _____Yes

----

23. Does .... ever suffer from constant or chronic bronchitis,
coughing, asthma, sinus trouble or hay fever?   _____No _____Yes

24. Does .... ever suffer from shortness of breath   _____No _____Yes

25. How many chest colds has .... had during the past year?   _____Number

26. Does .... usually cough up matter when he first gets up in
the morning?   _____No _____Yes

----

27. Has .... ever had or been suspected of having rheumatic fever?   _____No _____Yes

28. Has .... ever been diagnosed as having heart trouble?   _____No _____Yes

----

29. Does .... have an obvious jaw deformity?   _____No _____Yes

(IF OVER SIX YEARS OLD ASK:)
30. Do .... teeth fail to come together for proper chewing or are
they very crooked?   _____No _____Yes

----

31. Has .... ever had any serious trouble with skin rashes, eczema
or acne or similar skin trouble?   _____No _____Yes

32. Does .... have any unsightly birthmark, discoloration of the
skin or other skin deformity?   _____No _____Yes

33. Has .... ever suffered from serious trouble with boils or
carbuncles or a like skin trouble?   _____No _____Yes

If answer is "Yes" to 31, 32, or 33, ask:
What are .... symptoms? (circle above or describe)

_____

_____

_____

----

34. Has .... had any condition present since birth that we have
not asked about?   _____No _____Yes

If answer is "Yes," describe in detail: _____

_____

_____

_____

35. Does .... have anything wrong with him at all that you know of
and that we have not asked about?   _____No _____Yes

If answer is "Yes," describe the trouble in detail: _____

_____

_____

_____

36. Is .... (a) _____ Confined to the house except for emergencies?

         (b) _____ Able to go outside but needs the help of another person in getting
                   around outside?

         (c) _____ Able to go outside alone but has trouble in getting around freely?

         (d) _____ Not limited in any of these ways?

If (a), (b), or (c), WHY? in detail_____

37. (ASK FOR PERSONS 17 YEARS AND OLDER EXCEPT HOUSEWIVES AND SCHOOLCHILDREN)
Is .... (a) _____ Not able to work at all at present?

         (b) _____ Able to work but limited in amount or kind of work?

         (c) _____ Able to work but limited in kind or amount of other activities?

         (d) _____ Not limited in any of these ways?

If (a), (b), or (c), WHY? in detail _____

38. (ASK FOR PERSONS WHO ARE HOUSEWIVES)
Is .... (a) _____ Not able to keep house at all at present?

         (b) _____ Able to keep house but limited in amount or kind of housework?

         (c) _____ Able to keep house but limited in kind or amount of other activities?

         (d) _____ Not limited in any of these ways?

If (a), (b), or (c), WHY? in detail_____

39. (ASK FOR CHILDREN FROM 6 THROUGH 16 YEARS OLD)
Is .... (a) _____ Not able to go to school at all at the present time?

    (b) ,_____ Able to go to school but limited to certain types of schools or in school attendance?

    (c) _____ Able to go to school but limited in other activities?

    (d) _____ Not limited in any of these ways?

If (a), (b), or (c), WHY? in detail _____

_____

40. (ASK FOR CHILDREN UNDER 6 YEARS OLD)
Is .... (a) _____ Not able to take part at all in ordinary play with other children?

    (b) _____ Able to play with other children but limited in amount or kind of play?

    (c) _____ Not limited in any of these ways?

If (a) or (b), WHY? in detail_____

_____

NORTH CAROLINA SURVEY OF HANDICAPPED CHILDREN
INDIVIDUAL DATA SHEET

Name of child _____ Date of birth _____
                last name   first name   middle name   mo.   date   year

Sex: M___ F___ Race of child: _____ Is child known by teacher? Yes____ No ____

Name of parents or guardian _____

Address of parents or guardian _____

Part I.

Please check the item(s) which describe(s) the defect(s) or condition of the child.

___ 1. Poor balance or coordination
___ 2. Poor use of arms and hands
___ 3. Poor use of legs and feet
___ 4. Unusual jerking of arms, legs, face or body
___ 5. Arms, legs, feet, hands, face, or body pulled into a peculiar position
___ 6. Known to have seizures or convulsions
___ 7. Severe sight difficulty or blind
___ 8. Severe hearing difficulty or deaf
___ 9. Hare lip and/or cleft palate (corrected or not)
___ 10. Severe emotional problem (either aggressive and outward or withdrawn and retiring
___ 11. Speech disorders (stutters, baby talk, lisping, poor volume control, flat mono-
           tone, nasal tones or other distorted speech sounds)
___ 12. Mentally handicapped (please check the applicable sub-items on mentally retarded
           children.)
                  ___ a. Educable mentally retarded (I.Q. 51-75)
                  ___ b. Trainable mentally retarded (I.Q. 25-50)
                  ___ c. Appears to be mentally retarded, but no test scores
                         available

___ 13. Other_____
                         write in any other condition not covered above

Part II.

Please check the item which explains the child's situation regarding training or
education.

CHILD IS LIVING AT HOME AND IS: CHILD IS LIVING AWAY FROM HOME AT A:
___ 1. Under school age   ___ 1. Private special school
___ 2. Attending public school in regular classes   ___ 2. State supported special school
___ 3. Attending public school in special classes   ___ 3. Hospital or hospital school
___ 4. Receiving education at home   ___ 4. Other
___ 5. Attending hospital school
___ 6. Of school age, but receiving no education
       or training
___ 7. Over school age

If child is attending a school (public, private, hospital, etc.) please specify the
name and address in the space provided.

Name of school or institution: _____

Address of school or institution: _____

Name of teacher supplying information: _____

Name of school in which teacher is employed: _____

North Carolina Survey of Handicapped Children
Special School Survey

INFORMATION CONCERNING SURVEY

This is a survey of the handicapped children of Alamance County. It is similar to a survey completed two years ago by the United Cerebral Palsy, Inc., of North Carolina which was state-wide in scope. This replication and continuation of their efforts is designed to test the consistency of such surveys. The present study is sponsored by the Nemours Foundation of Wilmington, Delaware, the University of North Carolina, and the North Carolina Health Council.

The goal of the study will be to survey each of the public schools in North Carolina. The objectives of the study are:

1. To discover the number of children, under 21 years of age, in the state of North Carolina who are handicapped according to the categories stated on the Individual Data Sheet.

2. To follow-up with a clinical survey in certain selected areas and to place in the hands of the local superintendent of public schools and other appropriate agencies the information on all the handicapped children identified in the survey.

3. To bring to the attention of the public the facts on these children in the hope that it will lead to better treatment, care and education of them.

4. To obtain data on the causes of cerebral palsy in the hope that the knowledge gained will make it possible to reduce the occurrence of these handicapping conditions in the future.

GUIDE FOR TEACHERS

There are two steps to be carried out by each individual teacher. The first is for each teacher to check carefully the children in his or her homeroom to determine if any boy or girl has one or more of the handicapping conditions listed in the Individual Data Sheet on Handicapped Children. If any are identified, the teacher is asked to fill out IN DUPLICATE an Individual Data Sheet on each handicapped child.

The second step is concerned with the handicapped children who are not attending public schools. It is requested that public school children at the 4th grade level and above be asked to report to the homeroom teacher any handicapped children in their neighborhood who are not attending public schools. Children identified in this way are to be reported in the same manner and on the same forms (IN DUPLICATE) as are those attending public schools.

CLINIC COVER SHEET

INFORMATION AND EVALUATION	CODE

1. NAME _____ 2. SERIAL NO. _____   _ _ _

3. AGE _____ 4. RACE _____ 5. SEX ____   _ _ _ _

6. CLINIC INVITED TO AND SOURCE OF INVITATION _____   _ _ _

7. SOCIAL HISTORY:

    ASSESSMENT OF FAMILY RELATIONSHIPS _____   _

    ASSESSMENT OF FAMILY FINANCES _____   _

    NUMBER OF SIBLINGS _____   _

    NUMBER OF HANDICAPPED IN HOME _____   _

    MOTHER WORKING? _____   _

8. AGENCIES BY WHICH CHILD HAS BEEN TREATED AND DIAGNOSIS AS REPORTED BY PARENT:

    FIRST _____   _ _ _ _

    SECOND _____   _ _ _ _

    THIRD _____   _ _ _ _

9. INTELLIGENCE QUOTIENT AND BASIS OF ESTIMATE _____   _ _ _

10. STATURE:

    HEIGHT _____   _

    ESTIMATE OF PHYSICAL CONDITION _____   _

11. CLINICAL DIAGNOSIS AND ESTIMATE OF SEVERITY OF CONDITION:

    FIRST _____   _ _ _ _

    SECOND _____   _ _ _ _

    THIRD _____   _ _ _ _

    FOURTH _____   _ _ _ _

    FIFTH _____   _ _ _ _

12. ESTIMATE OF HANDICAP _____   _

13. ESTIMATE OF VOCATIONAL HANDICAP _____   _

CLINIC COVER SHEET - Agencies

NAME _____   SERIAL NUMBER _____   SURVEY _____

Clinic diagnosis

Agencies

Diagnoses

148

North Carolina Survey of Handicapped Children

PEDIATRIC EXAMINATION

Vital Signs	T P R Wt % Ht % BP(above 2 years)

General	Development WD, FWD, PD		Nourishment WN, FWN, PN
	Color		Distress

Skin	Rash	Pigment	Hair

Head	Symmetry	Anterior fontanelle	Occipito-frontal circumference
	& shape		

Eyes	EOM	Pupils reaction to L&A	Icterus Conjunctivitis
	Ptosis of lids	Funduscopy	

Ears	Canals	MT's	Hearing-screening test

Nose	Septal deviation	Mucous membranes	Tonsils

Lymph nodes	GGE	Cervicals, suboccipitals, axillary, epitrochlear, inguinal

Neck	stiffness

Chest	Symmetry	Character of breathing	P&A

Heart	LBCD	Character of sounds	Rhythm Murmurs
	Thrills		

Abdomen	Liver Spleen	Masses Umbilical hernia Inguinal hernia

Genitalia	Appearance	Scrotal contents	Phimosis Vaginal discharge

Skeletal	Scoliosis	Kyphosis	Lordosis Mobility of joints
	Muscle strength	Extremities	especially hips

Neurological	Cranial nerves	Speech
	Motor tone	
	Strength and coordination	Gait
	Sensation to touch	pain position
	Abdominal reflexes	DTR's Plantar response

        Handedness   Mixed dominance

Remarks: _____
_____
_____
_____
_____
_____

Refer to: _____

North Carolina Survey of Handicapped Children

MEDICAL HISTORY

Name _____ Age ____ Sex ____ Race ____ Date ____

History of disability (Give date of illness or injury or when handicap first noted, affected part or extent of illness. Summarize treatment given and source)

_____
_____
_____
_____

FAMILY HISTORY:

Presence of: Tuberculosis ____ Diabetes ____ Syphilis ____ Heart Disease ____ Asthma ____

Asthma ____ Neurological conditions ____ Other _____

Is there a condition similar to child's in family? No ____ Yes ____ If yes, specify: _____

_____

MOTHER's PREGNANCIES:

Number full term ____ Premature ____ Miscarriages ____ Interruptions ____

Ages of siblings: Dead (State cause) _____

Living _____

Condition of mother during THIS pregnancy: Well ____ Toxemia ____ Hypertension ____ Acute

disease ____ Other _____

Remarks:_____

_____

HISTORY OF BIRTH:

Para ____ of _____ Parents related?_____

Delivered by _____ Home ____ Hospital_____

Hours in labor: Normal _____ Prolonged _____ Precipitate_____

Presentation: Head _____ Breech _____ Other _____

Type of Delivery: Normal ____ Instruments ____ Cesearian ____ Cord about neck _____

Special circumstances and remarks:_____

_____

Birth: Full term ____ Late ____ Multiple ____ Premature (mos.) ____ Weight _____

Conditions at birth: Normal ____ Blue baby ____ Resusicitation necessary ____

Weak ____ Convulsions ____ Evidence of head trauma ____ Other injuries ____ incu-

bator ____ how long?____ Weak cry ____ Jaundice ____ How long? ____ Other _____

Remarks:_____

Medical History

Name_____

DEVELOPMENTAL HISTORY:

Age (months and years) at which first:

Held head up_____

Rolled over _____

Sat alone_____

Stood alone_____

Walked without support_____

Speech: Normal ___ Delayed ___ Stutter ___

Other _____

Bowel Control: Day _____

Night_____

Bladder Control: Day _____

Night _____

HANDEDNESS: R or L now _____ Age showing preference_____

Any left handedness in family? _____

Remarks:_____

_____

GENERAL HEALTH AND FEEDING RECORD:

As infant, was there a feeding problem? ____ Vomiting ___ Colic ___

Breast fed ____ How long _____ Formula _____ Vitamins _____

Constipation _____ Trouble feeding or swallowing _____

Present feeding schedule _____ Feeding hours _____

Eating between meals _____

Appetite: Excellent _____ Good _____ Poor _____

Check each past illness: Measles ___ Whooping Cough ___ Chicken Pox ___ Mumps ___ Diph-

theria ___ Scarlet Fever ___ Poliomyelitis ___ Tonsilitis ___

Colds ___ Otitis Media ___ Asthma ___ Eczema ___ Hay fever ___

Rheumatic Fever ___ Other _____

Operations: Tonsillectomy and Adenoidectomy _____ Other _____

Accidents _____

PRESENT STATUS:

Bright ___ Dull ___ Apathetic ___

General Appearance: Average _____ Nervous _____ Retarded _____

Talking: Normal _____ Words _____ Sentences _____ Intelligible _____

Unintelligible _____

Toilet Trained: Bowels _____ Bladder _____

Feeds Self: With help _____ Alone _____ Dresses Self: With help_____ Alone _____

Understands: Everything _____ Less than normal _____ very little_____

Drooling: Yes _____ No _____

Medical History   Page 3

PRESENT STATUS (continued)

Eyes Involved: Squint Yes _____ No _____

                Vision Yes _____ No _____

Hearing Involved: Yes _____ No _____

Trunk Involved: Yes _____ No _____

Legs Involved: Yes R - L   No R - L

Arms Involved: Yes R - L   No R - L

CONVULSIONS

* (Describe character and frequency, if present. Note whether they occur with or without fever. Note if medication given and response to medication) _____

_____

_____

_____

_____

* Use Special Form for Convulsion History - Epilepsy Clinic.

Data collected by: _____

Date _____

SOCIAL SERVICE

Patient's Name _____ Date _____

Age _____ Race _____ Sex _____

I. FAMILY COMPOSITION

A. Parents

1. Both parents in home _____	5. Stepmother _____
2. Mother only _____	6. Relatives _____
3. Father only _____	7. Foster home _____
4. Stepfather _____	8. Institution _____

Remarks: _____

_____

B. Economic Situation   Good Fair Poor   Irrelevant or unable to determine - reasons

	Good	Fair	Poor	Irrelevant or unable to determine - reasons
1. Income				
2. Housing				

Remarks: _____

Summation of Item I. _____

_____

_____

_____

II. ATTITUDES AND RELATIONSHIPS

A. Patient

1. Maturity

	Good	Fair	Poor	Irrelevant or unable to determine - reasons
(1) Poise				
(2) Relationship with mother				
(3) Relationship with father				
(4) Relationship with siblings				
(5) Relationship with other children				
(6) Relationship with teacher				

2. Attitude Toward Handicap

	Good	Fair	Poor	Irrelevant or unable to determine - reasons
(1) Understanding of Condition				
(2) Desire for treatment				
(3) Attitude toward disability				
(4) (a) Resentment				
(b) Feeling of stigma				
(c) Guilt				
(d) Ability to accept in its reality				
(e) Ability to accept reasonable goals in				
Play				
School				
Employment				
Rehabilitation				
(f) Dependency				

Remarks: _____

Social Service   Name_____

B. Father	Good	Fair	Poor	Irrelevant or unable to obtain - reason
1. Understanding of condition				
2. Reasonable acceptance				
3. Feelings of				
(1) Guilt				
(2) Stigma				
(3) Denial				
4. Ability to accept reasonable goals in				
(1) Play or employment				
(2) School				
(3) Rehabilitation				

C. Mother

	Good	Fair	Poor	
1. Understanding of condition				
2. Reasonable acceptance				
3. Feelings of				
(1) Guilt				
(2) Stigma				
(3) Denial				
4. Ability to accept reasonable goals in				
(1) Play or employment				
(2) School				
(3) Rehabilitation				

D. Impact of Disability Upon

1. Relationship of parents				
2. Siblings				

Remarks:_____
_____
_____
_____

Summation of Item II._____
_____
_____
_____
_____
_____
_____
_____

Social Service

Name_____

III. Education

	Past	Present	Needed
A. Regular class			
B. Regular class - modified program			
C. Special class			
D. Home instruction			
E. Hospital instruction			
F. Vocational instruction			
1. Trade School			
2. Apprentice			
G. Special School			
1. Blind			
2. Deaf			
3. Speech			
4. Mental defective			

H. Appraisal	Good	Fair	Poor	Unable to determine - reason
1. Progress in School				
2. Academic Rating				

Summation of Item III_____

_____

_____

_____

_____

_____

_____

IV. EMPLOYMENT

1. Present employment
   (a) By whom employed?
   (b) In what capacity?
   (c) How long on present job?
   (d) Monthly wage

2. Past employment

	First job	Second job	Third job	Fourth job
(a) Name of employer				
(b) How long employed				
(c) Reason for change				

3. Recommendations for job placement
   (a) Regular placement
   (b) Special placement
   (c) Sheltered workshop

Summation of Item IV:_____

_____

_____

_____

_____

_____

_____

_____

_____

155

Social Service   Name_____

V. FACTORS AFFECTING SOCIAL ACCEPTABILITY

   1. Accessory movements_____
   2. Bowel and bladder control_____
   3. Braces_____
   4. Bragging_____
   5. Convulsions_____
   6. Condition of teeth_____
   7. Crutches_____
   8. Discharge from ears_____
   9. Drooling_____
  10. Emotional disturbance_____
  11. Eyes_____
  12. Gait_____
  13. Grimaces_____
  14. Hearing_____
  15. Irritability_____
  16. Jaw deformity_____
  17. Mental retardation_____
  18. Obesity_____
  19. Posture_____
  20. Prosthesis - arm, leg_____
  21. Ptosis_____
  22. Scars visible_____
  23. Speech disturbance_____
  24. Squint or frown_____
  25. Submissiveness_____
  26. Timidity_____
  27. Very thin_____
  28. Wheezing or coughing_____
  29. Skin condition_____
  30. Other - itemize_____

Summation of Item V:

156

ALAMANCE COUNTY CHILD HEALTH STUDY

.To the Superintendent of Schools Burlington
                                   Alamance County :

_____ is one of the

children to be examined in our child health study on the morning of ____
                                                          afternoon

_____. We will appreciate his being excused for this purpose.

Sincerely,

William P. Richardson, M. D.
Director

ALAMANCE COUNTY CHILD HEALTH STUDY

Survey Clinic Form

I hereby authorize the staff of the Child Health Survey to make known to the
appropriate local agencies and physicians findings from this survey.

My physicians' name(s) is (are):

_____

_____

_____

_____
Signature of parent or guardian